WELCOME TO

HOW IT WORKS

60 SECOND SCIENCE

Welcome to How It Works 60 Second Science. In this fact-packed guide we introduce fundamental principles in physics, biology and chemistry with clear, concise explanations, infographics and illustrations. From the Big Bang to quantum mechanics, and fossils to Wi-Fi, you'll be up to speed with the latest breakthroughs in no time. Throughout the book you'll also have the opportunity to put these theories into practice with our easy-to-follow experiments. See how circuits work with batteries made from lemons, detect Earth's magnetic field by making your own compass, learn how to instantly freeze water with a single touch, and much more.
So what are you waiting for? Dive in to discover how the wonderful world around you works.

FUTURE

Future PLC Quay House, The Ambury, Bath, BA1 1UA

Bookazine Editorial
Editor **Jacqueline Snowden**
Design **Ali Innes, Jordan Travers**
Compiled by **Dan Peel & Adam Markiewicz**
Senior Art Editor **Andy Downes**
Head of Art & Design **Greg Whitaker**
Editorial Director **Jon White**

How It Works Editorial
Editor **Ben Biggs**
Senior Art Editor **Duncan Crook**

Contributors
Briony Duguid, Laura Mears, Laurie Newman

Cover images
Getty Images

Photography
Getty Images
All copyrights and trademarks are recognised and respected

Advertising
Media packs are available on request
Commercial Director **Clare Dove**

International
Head of Print Licensing **Rachel Shaw**
licensing@futurenet.com
www.futurecontenthub.com

Circulation
Head of Newstrade **Tim Mathers**

Production
Head of Production **Mark Constance**
Production Project Manager **Matthew Eglinton**
Advertising Production Manager **Joanne Crosby**
Digital Editions Controller **Jason Hudson**
Production Managers **Keely Miller, Nola Cokely,**
Vivienne Calvert, Fran Twentyman

Printed in the UK

Distributed by Marketforce, 5 Churchill Place, Canary Wharf, London, E14 5HU
www.marketforce.co.uk Tel: 0203 787 9001

60 Second Science Fifth Edition (HIB4878)
© 2022 Future Publishing Limited

All content previously appeared in this edition of
60 Second Science

We are committed to only using magazine paper which is derived from responsibly managed, certified forestry and chlorine-free manufacture. The paper in this bookazine was sourced and produced from sustainable managed forests, conforming to strict environmental and socioeconomic standards.

All contents © 2022 Future Publishing Limited or published under licence. All rights reserved. No part of this magazine may be used, stored, transmitted or reproduced in any way without the prior written permission of the publisher. Future Publishing Limited (company number 2008885) is registered in England and Wales. Registered office: Quay House, The Ambury, Bath BA1 1UA. All information contained in this publication is for information only and is, as far as we are aware, correct at the time of going to press. Future cannot accept any responsibility for errors or inaccuracies in such information. You are advised to contact manufacturers and retailers directly with regard to the price of products/services referred to in this publication. Apps and websites mentioned in this publication are not under our control. We are not responsible for their contents or any other changes or updates to them. This magazine is fully independent and not affiliated in any way with the companies mentioned herein.

FUTURE

Connectors.
Creators.
Experience
Makers.

Future plc is a public
company quoted on the
London Stock Exchange
(symbol: FUTR)
www.futureplc.com

Chief executive **Zillah Byng-Thorne**
Non-executive chairman **Richard Huntingford**
Chief financial officer **Penny Ladkin-Brand**

Tel +44 (0)1225 442 244

Part of the

HOW IT WORKS
bookazine series

Widely
Recycled

ipso.
For press freedom
with responsibility

HOW IT WORKS
CONTENTS

008   **The Big Bang**

010   **Atomic structure**

012   **Electric currents**

016   **Cell division**

018   **States of matter**

022   **Nerve signals**

024   **Star life cycles**

026   **How fossils form**

030   **Doppler shift**

032   **Respiration**

036   **Special Relativity**

038   **General Relativity**

040   **Magnetism**

044   **How old are your cells?**

046   **Moments explained**

050   **How the heart beats**

052   **Photosynthesis**

054   **Planet formation**

058   **Newton's laws of motion**

060   **Archimedes' principle**

064   **Internal combustion engines**

066   **Bacteria and viruses**

068   **How light behaves**

072   **Vitamins and minerals**

074   **Hydraulic systems**

076   **Earth's structure**

078   **The laws of thermodynamics**

080   **Your body's elements**

082   **Quantum mechanics**

084   **Wi-Fi explained**

088   **The periodic table**

090   **Inside the human brain**

092   **Crystallography**

096   **Nuclear fission and fusion**

098   **The forces of nature**

102   **The scale of your body's cells**

40
Magnetism

12
Electric currents

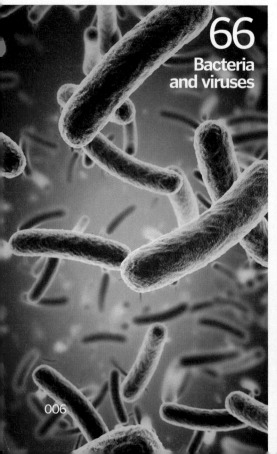

66
Bacteria and viruses

54
Planet formation

90
The human brain

72
Vitamins and minerals

58
Newton's laws of motion

44
How old are your cells?

TRY IT YOURSELF...

014	Build a lemon battery circuit
020	Instantly freeze water
028	Make your own fossils
034	Build a model lung
042	Make a compass
048	Build a bridge
056	Make a planetary system model
062	Build a bubble bottle
070	Split the colours of light
086	How to boost your Wi-Fi
094	Make geode crystals
100	Build a teddy bear zip wire
108	Create a solar tower
114	Make an electric motor
122	Build a speaker
126	Make pH paper

104	How GPS works		116	Enzymes explained
106	Heat transfer		118	Water transport in plants
110	How the body digests food		120	Sound waves
112	Electricity and magnetism		124	Acids and alkalis

The Big Bang Theory

TAKE A TRIP BACK IN TIME TO FIND OUT HOW EVERYTHING BEGAN

We can still see the first light of the universe as cosmic microwave background radiation

The universe began when a dense speck burst apart in a blaze of heat. Everything rushed outwards and, as it expanded, it started to cool. Within minutes, the temperature had dropped to billions of degrees, allowing the first particles to come together. They formed a cloud so thick and hot that no light could pass through it.

After 400,000 years it became cool enough for atoms to form. For the first time, light could travel through space and the universe became transparent. For hundreds of millions of years, atoms gathered together as patches of gas. Gravity tugged them into ever expanding clumps that became denser and hotter until there was enough energy for atoms to fuse.

Then, the first stars were born. It took a billion more years for the stars to form galaxies, and they've been evolving ever since, still hurtling away from the explosion that happened all those years ago.

The first galaxies started forming around 400,000 years after the Big Bang

BACKGROUND

You'd have to travel 14 billion years back in time to see the start of the universe but, even if time travel were possible, you wouldn't survive for long. There was no time, no space and the entirety of existence took up no more room than an atom. Then, everything exploded; in a flash of energy, the universe burst into life. Within fractions of a second, it had ballooned to the size of a galaxy and it's been expanding ever since.

FIRST LIGHT

For the first 400,000 years, the universe was so hot and so full of matter that no light could get through. But when it had cooled enough for atoms to form, it became transparent. On that day, light started to travel across space, and it's still travelling now. The universe has been expanding for all that time, which has stretched the radiation, so it no longer looks like the light we're used to.

Invisible to the naked eye, the earliest light in the universe now travels as microwaves with a temperature just above absolute zero. This ancient light reveals that, although the early universe was quite smooth, there were little lumps and bumps that contained slightly more or slightly less matter than the surrounding sky. These ripples created pockets of gas, which clumped together to form stars, shaping the universe that we see today.

THE HISTORY OF THE UNIVERSE

Track the life of the universe from its birth to the present day

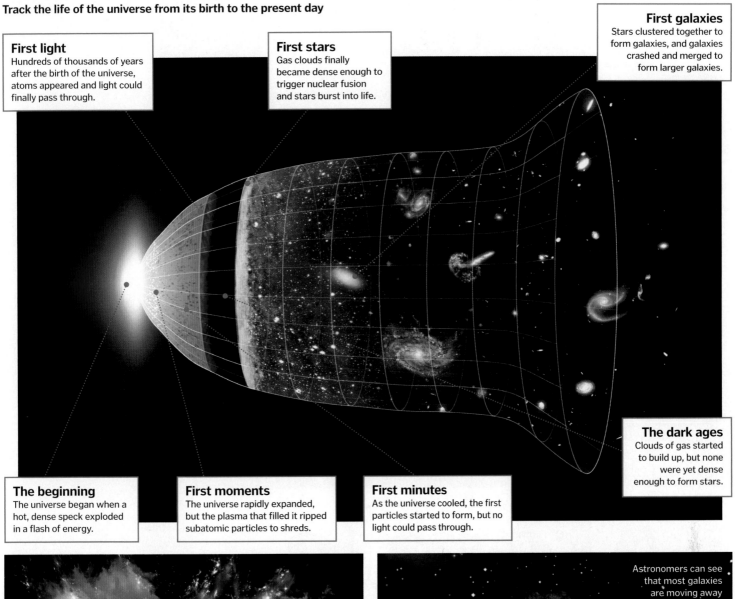

First light
Hundreds of thousands of years after the birth of the universe, atoms appeared and light could finally pass through.

First stars
Gas clouds finally became dense enough to trigger nuclear fusion and stars burst into life.

First galaxies
Stars clustered together to form galaxies, and galaxies crashed and merged to form larger galaxies.

The dark ages
Clouds of gas started to build up, but none were yet dense enough to form stars.

The beginning
The universe began when a hot, dense speck exploded in a flash of energy.

First moments
The universe rapidly expanded, but the plasma that filled it ripped subatomic particles to shreds.

First minutes
As the universe cooled, the first particles started to form, but no light could pass through.

Some scientists predict that the Big Bang came after a 'Big Crunch' in a universal cycle of contraction and expansion

Astronomers can see that most galaxies are moving away from us, meaning that the universe must be expanding

SUMMARY

The universe began with a monumental explosion that created space and time. Particles formed first, then atoms, then stars, and finally galaxies. It's been expanding outwards ever since.

Atomic structure

BREAK OPEN THE BUILDING BLOCKS OF THE UNIVERSE AND SEE WHAT'S INSIDE

All the matter in the universe is made up of atoms. At the heart of every atom is the atomic nucleus; a cluster of protons and neutrons so small that we talk about their mass and charge in relative terms. Both have a relative mass of one, protons have a relative charge of plus one and neutrons a relative charge of zero. Together, they make up almost all the mass of the atom, but they only take up a tiny fraction of its total diameter. The rest of the space occupied by atoms is the domain of the electrons. These tiny particles have a relative charge of minus one, enough to balance out one proton, but they only have a relative mass of just 0.0005. They swirl around the nucleus in rings called shells.

> "The structure of atoms explains why elements behave differently"

BACKGROUND

The idea that tiny building blocks make up the universe has been around since the ancient Greeks. They used the word 'atom', which literally means uncuttable, to describe the chemical building blocks that make up everything we see. But it wasn't until the 1800s that scientists started to unravel how atoms work.

The structure of atoms tells us why different chemical elements behave in different ways, and helps to explain some of the fundamental forces that govern our universe.

KEY FIGURES

Physicist JJ Thomson came up with one of the earliest models of what an atom might look like; in 1897 he discovered electrons, and thought that they might sit inside an atom like raisins in a cake. But his 'plum pudding' model – proposed in 1904 – didn't last long.

A few years later Ernest Rutherford discovered that particles could pass straight through gold foil, meaning that atoms contain empty space. Positively charged particles mostly passed through the foil in a straight line, but some bent sideways. This revealed that the solid parts of atoms, the nuclei, had a positive charge. So, the electrons had to be outside the nucleus, and there needed to be enough space between them to let particles pass through.

To explain this, in 1913 Niels Bohr came up with an atomic diagram that showed electrons moving around the nucleus in rings.

INSIDE AN ATOM

Every element has the same basic core structure

Electron
Negatively charged electrons have a relative charge of -1 and a relative mass of 0.0005.

Shell
Electrons orbit the nucleus in shells. The Bohr model of the atom depicts electrons like planets orbiting a star.

Atomic number
The atomic number of an atom tells you how many protons it has.

Proton
Positively charged protons have a relative charge of +1 and a relative mass of 1.

+ Proton

O Neutron

▬ Electron

Nucleus
The solid core of an atom, the nucleus, contains the protons and neutrons.

Neutron
Neutral neutrons have a relative charge of 0 and a relative mass of 1.

Mass number
The mass number of an atom tells you how many protons and neutrons it has.

Physical models help scientists visualise how atoms are arranged within molecules

Danish physicist Niels Bohr thought electrons moved around atoms in rings

SUMMARY

Positive protons and neutral neutrons have a relative mass of one and exist in the atomic nucleus. Negative electrons have a relative mass of 0.0005 and exist in clouds around the nucleus.

© Getty

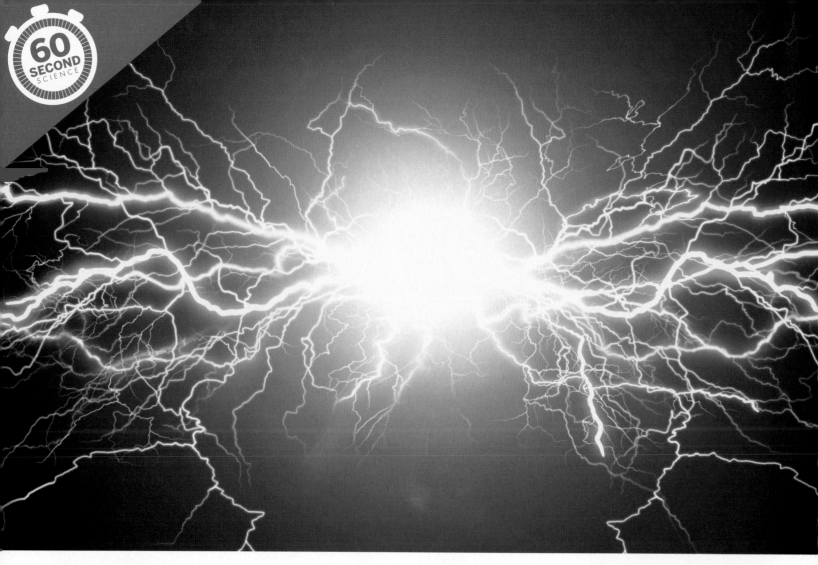

Electricity explained

THE SHOCKING SCIENCE OF CIRCUITS, CURRENTS AND VOLTS

Electricity is generated by the flow of electrons. Some of the first experiments with electricity were performed by the ancient Greeks, who observed that if you rubbed amber against fur, it would attract dust and other small particles. In fact, the word electricity is derived from the Greek word for amber – elektron.

For electrons to move around and create a current, there has to be a circuit. This is a closed loop that allows a steady flow of electrons, carrying tiny amounts of electrical energy as they go. Circuits can be created using any conductive substances. They can be made using solid materials like copper wire and other metals (which have free electrons to carry the charge), but they can also be made from fluids containing charged ions, such as the salty fluid in our bodies, or from gases, such as air during a lightning strike.

However, a circuit on its own is not enough to produce an electric current; a voltage, or potential difference, is needed to get things moving. This can be provided by a battery, a generator, or by the build-up of static.

BACKGROUND

Electricity is a form of energy, and in combination with magnetism, it makes up one of the four fundamental forces of the physical world. It is generated by the movement of electrons, which are subatomic particles that orbit the nuclei of every atom.

In many materials, such as wood and plastic, electrons are held tightly alongside their atoms, but in some materials, such as metal, they can break free and move around on their own. Electrons have a negative charge, and it is the movement of this charge that creates electricity.

KEY FIGURES

It wasn't until the 17th and 18th centuries that the science of electricity started to emerge. At first, it was thought that electricity was a fluid, and Dutch scientists built 'Leyden jars' to contain it. The glass jars had metal inside and out, and could store a static charge.

In 1752, American polymath Benjamin Franklin described an experiment to demonstrate that lightning was electricity: by flying a kite with a key attached to its string during a thunderstorm. In the 1800s, Italian scientist Alessandro Volta discovered that electrical potential could cause an electrical charge to flow. He used this knowledge to invent batteries.

HOW A CIRCUIT WORKS

Discover the key components in a simple electrical circuit

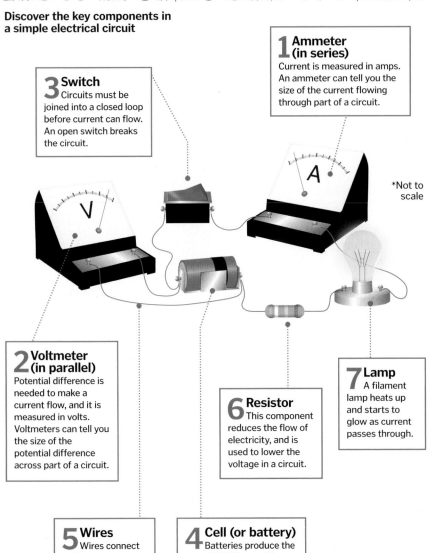

3 Switch
Circuits must be joined into a closed loop before current can flow. An open switch breaks the circuit.

1 Ammeter (in series)
Current is measured in amps. An ammeter can tell you the size of the current flowing through part of a circuit.

*Not to scale

2 Voltmeter (in parallel)
Potential difference is needed to make a current flow, and it is measured in volts. Voltmeters can tell you the size of the potential difference across part of a circuit.

6 Resistor
This component reduces the flow of electricity, and is used to lower the voltage in a circuit.

7 Lamp
A filament lamp heats up and starts to glow as current passes through.

5 Wires
Wires connect up the components, providing a path for electrons moving around the circuit.

4 Cell (or battery)
Batteries produce the potential difference that drives electrons around the circuit.

"For electrons to move around and create a current, there has to be a circuit"

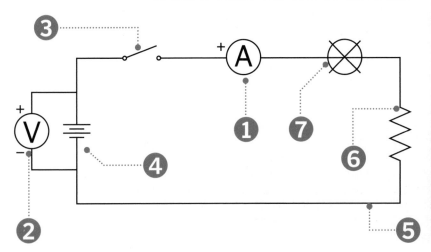

In the 1700s, US Founding Father Benjamin Franklin proposed an experiment to show that lightning is electricity

Without knowledge of electricity, modern life as we know it would be impossible

SUMMARY

Electricity is produced by the movement of charged particles – electrons or ions. It requires a complete circuit to flow, and it needs a potential difference to get the electrons moving.

© Getty

Make a lemon battery

HOW YOU CAN POWER AN LED BULB WITH SOME CITRUS FRUITS

1 Add the electrodes

For this experiment you will need: four lemons, an LED light, a multimeter, four galvanised nails, four copper coins and five wires with crocodile clips.

Cut two parallel slits a couple of centimetres apart in one side of the lemon. In one hole, slot in a copper coin, which will act as the positive electrode, and in the other place a galvanised nail (a nail that is coated in zinc), which will be the negative electrode. Make sure the two do not come into contact with each other inside the lemon, and then repeat the process with three more lemons.

2 Join the batteries

Connect the lemons together using three crocodile clipped copper wires. Clip one end of the first wire to the coin in the first lemon, then clip the other end to the nail in the next lemon. Repeat this along the line with the other two wires until they are all joined together. This will help to accumulate the power produced by the batteries so it is enough to power a bulb.

3 Measure the charge

Test that your battery works using a multimeter, an instrument that measures voltage. Attach two additional crocodile clipped copper wires to the remaining coin and nail at either end of your battery line-up, then connect the free ends to the multimeter. If it gives a reading of around 3.50 volts then you have set up your experiment correctly. If not, then repeat steps one and two.

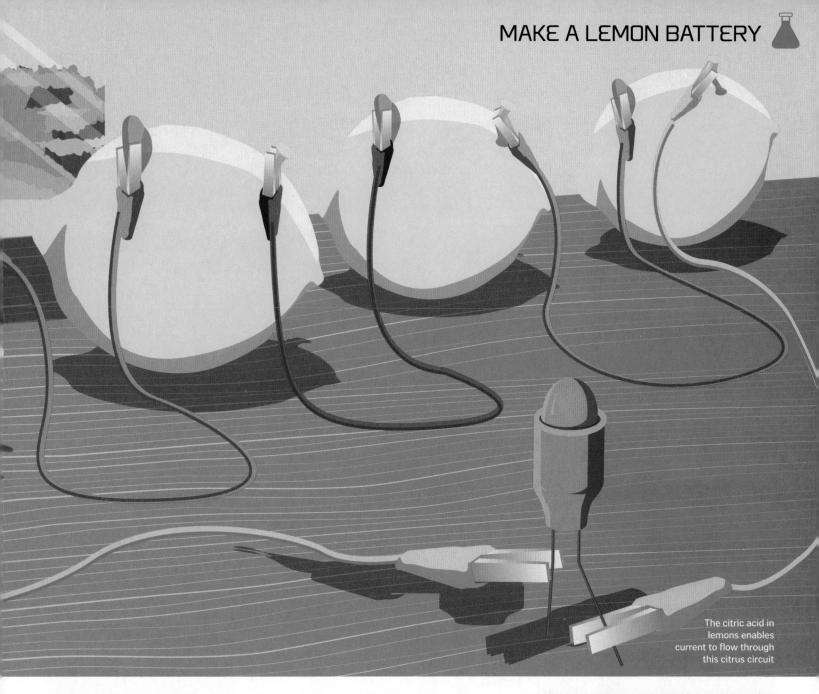

The citric acid in lemons enables current to flow through this citrus circuit

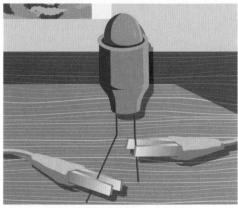

4 Connect the bulb

Disconnect the multimeter and connect the free ends of the copper wires to an LED bulb. Make sure you connect the wire leading from the furthest right-hand coin to the negative connector of the LED and the wire leading from the furthest left-hand nail to the positive connector. The negative and positive connectors of the LED should be labelled with – and + signs.

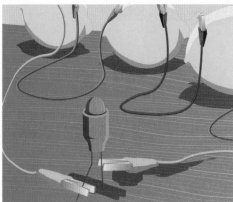

5 Light it up

Now your circuit is complete and the LED bulb should light up using the power generated from your lemon batteries. If you don't have four lemons handy, you can still try the experiment: place all four copper coins and galvanised nails into the same lemon, making sure they don't touch each other, and connect them in the same way – this will help to generate more power.

SUMMARY

Batteries convert stored chemical energy into electricity. They are essentially made of two electrodes, one positive and one negative, and a conductive solution called an electrolyte. When a battery is added to a circuit, this solution kick-starts an oxidisation process, allowing ions to move from the positively charged electrode to the negatively charged electrode, creating a flow of charge, or electricity.

In this lemon battery circuit, the citric acid in the lemon juice acts as the electrolyte, the coin is the positive electrode and the nail is the negative electrode.

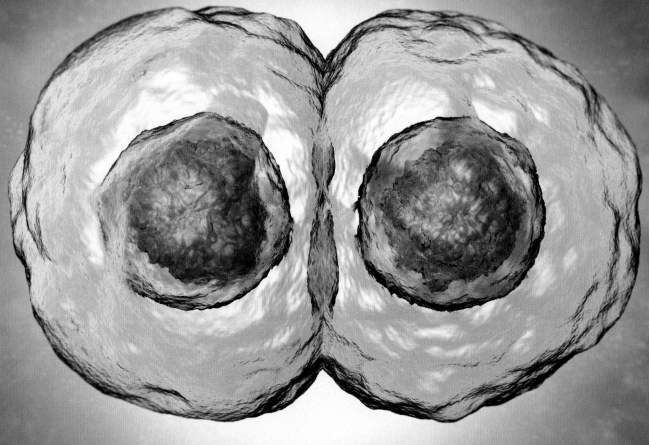

Cell division

GET TO GRIPS WITH MITOSIS AND MEIOSIS

There are two types of cell division: mitosis and meiosis. The single cell that starts it contains 23 pairs of chromosomes, one set from each parent. These are made from DNA, which stores genetic instructions. Each time a cell wants to divide, it needs to replicate this genetic code, and both types of cell division begin with the same step. The single DNA molecule of each chromosome is duplicated, forming a near-perfect copy.

If the cells are to be used for growth and repair in the body they will need a full set of instructions. Each new daughter cell receives two full sets of 23 chromosomes, essentially forming a clone of the original cell. This process is mitosis.

However, if the cells are going on to form sperm or eggs, they only need one set. This is so that when a sperm fertilises an egg, the resulting embryo has two complete sets, rather than four. This is meiosis.

BACKGROUND

The human body starts out as just a single cell, but by the time we are fully grown, we are made up of more than 37 trillion. Every second, millions of these cells die, and millions more are made to take their place. The process by which this happens is called cell division: one cell divides to become two, two divide to become four, four divide to become eight, and so on. It all starts with replication of the DNA genetic code.

CELL SIGNALS

Cell division must be controlled, so growth stops when we are big enough, and repair comes to an end when a wound is healed.

In 2001, three scientists were awarded the Nobel Prize in Physiology or Medicine for their work to uncover the mysteries of the cell cycle. Paul Nurse, Tim Hunt, and Leland Hartwell uncovered some of the key molecules responsible for driving cells through the different stages of division. They revealed the chemical 'start' button that kicks the cycle off, and uncovered some regulators that ensure each step happens in sequence. Understanding these processes has had a huge impact on other areas of science and medicine.

MITOSIS VS MEIOSIS

Both types of cell division begin in exactly the same way, but the end result is very different

Daughter cells
Each daughter cell made during mitosis receives two complete sets of chromosomes.

Parent cell
Before the cell begins to divide, each chromosome is made from one DNA molecule. They come in pairs, one from each parent.

DNA replication
The new cells will need their own copies of the DNA code, so the first step is to make duplicates.

Mitosis

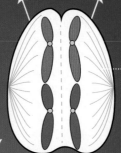

Mitosis
When cells are dividing for growth and repair, the duplicated chromosomes are split in two.

Meiosis

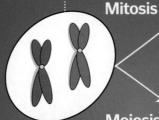
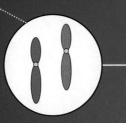

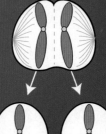
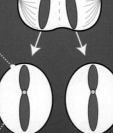

Meiosis I
When cells are dividing to make sperm or eggs, the chromosome pairs are separated first.

Meiosis II
The second stage is to split each chromosome in two, giving one copy of the DNA to each new cell.

Cell division involves duplicating DNA and then dividing it between daughter cells

Gametes
Sperm and egg cells have 23 chromosomes, but only one copy of each.

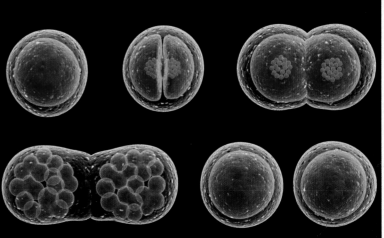

SUMMARY

There are two types of cell division. In mitosis, the daughter cells each get two full sets of chromosomes, but in meiosis, they each only get one.

States of matter

THE PHYSICS OF SOLIDS, LIQUIDS, GASES AND PLASMA EXPLAINED

The states of matter that we are all familiar with are solids, liquids and gases. The particles that make up solids are packed so tightly together that they barely move. They can be made up of mixtures of different atoms, or from repeating patterns of the same atoms that fit together to form crystals.

Liquids are looser. The particles are close together, but aren't in fixed positions. This means that they can flow. Gases are more loosely packed. The particles are far apart, and they move around rapidly in different directions, expanding to fill a container.

The fourth – and less familiar – state of matter is plasma. It is a bit like gas, but the atoms themselves have broken apart, becoming ionised and forming a sea of free electrons and atomic nuclei. Examples of plasma include lightning and neon signs.

BACKGROUND

Matter can exist in different forms depending on the environment. There are four fundamental states: solid, liquid, gas and plasma. In our daily lives, we are most familiar with the first three, but the most common state in the universe is actually plasma.

There are several other states of matter that are rarer, including Bose-Einstein condensates, quark-gluon plasma, and degenerate matter.

CHANGING STATES

In nature, matter can transition between the fundamental states, turning from plasma, to gas, to liquid, to solid and back again.

At cold temperatures, particles have little kinetic energy and are fixed in position, forming a solid. As the temperature increases, the particles gain energy and are able to move past each other. At this point the matter is in a liquid state. With a further temperature increase, the particles have enough energy to move freely, and the matter is a gas. Unless they are in a container, the atoms will spread out infinitely. If the atoms become hot enough, their electrons are stripped and they become plasma.

STATES OF WATER

On Earth, water naturally exists in all three states

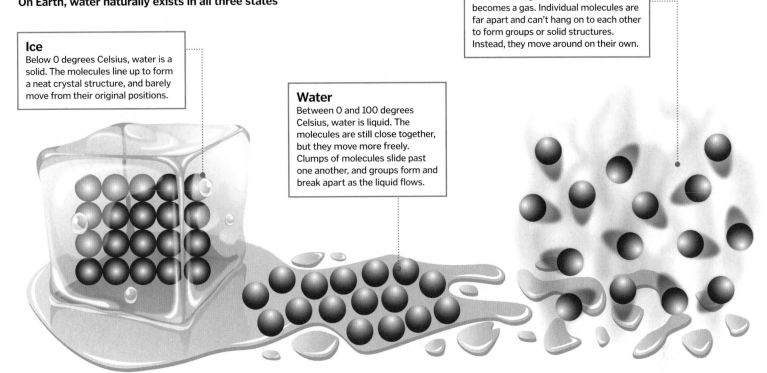

Ice
Below 0 degrees Celsius, water is a solid. The molecules line up to form a neat crystal structure, and barely move from their original positions.

Water
Between 0 and 100 degrees Celsius, water is liquid. The molecules are still close together, but they move more freely. Clumps of molecules slide past one another, and groups form and break apart as the liquid flows.

Steam
Above 100 degrees Celsius, water becomes a gas. Individual molecules are far apart and can't hang on to each other to form groups or solid structures. Instead, they move around on their own.

"As the temperature increases, the particles gain energy and are able to move past each other"

When water reaches its boiling point it starts to evaporate as steam

Water is unusual because it is less dense as a solid than as a liquid, which is why ice floats

SUMMARY

The main states of matter are solids, liquids and gases. Their properties differ; particles in solids are static, in liquids they move more freely, and in gases they move quickly in all directions.

© Getty

Freeze water in a flash

GET THE POWER OF A SUPERHERO AND FREEZE A GLASS OF WATER WITH A SINGLE TOUCH!

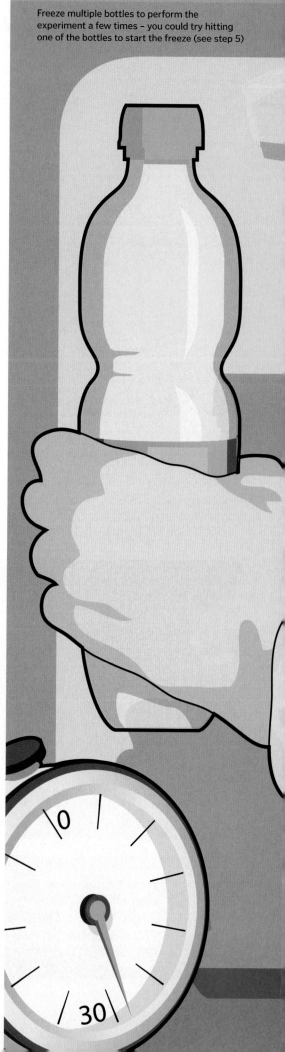

Freeze multiple bottles to perform the experiment a few times – you could try hitting one of the bottles to start the freeze (see step 5)

1 Cool your water

For this experiment you will need at least three bottles of purified water, a glass, a bowl of crushed ice and access to a freezer. First you need to freeze the water. You might think that you can make your own purified water for this experiment by boiling it for a few minutes, but that won't remove the chemicals in the liquid, so you'll need to buy specially purified water instead. Take three unopened 500ml plastic bottles of the water and place two of them in the freezer on their side.

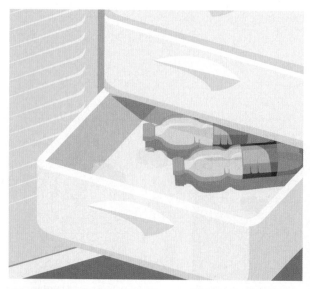

2 Be careful!

After 30 minutes put in a third bottle. Having more than one bottle will increase your chances of this working, so you can put in even more if you want to try the experiment a few times! You need to leave your water in the freezer for two hours and 15 minutes in total. Make sure to leave the water as undisturbed as possible while it's in your freezer, as agitation can start the crystallisation process.

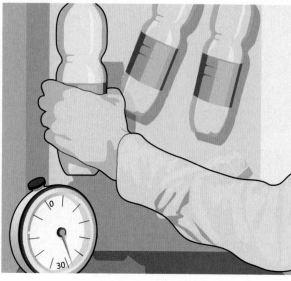

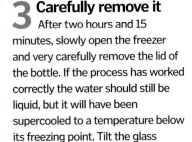

3 Carefully remove it

After two hours and 15 minutes, slowly open the freezer and very carefully remove the lid of the bottle. If the process has worked correctly the water should still be liquid, but it will have been supercooled to a temperature below its freezing point. Tilt the glass you're going to use and slowly pour the water into the glass. If you're careful, the supercooled liquid shouldn't start to solidify.

4 Grab some ice

You'll need the crushed ice for this part. Put your finger into the crushed ice and make sure that there's at least one ice crystal stuck to your fingertip. That's all it will take to start the crystallisation process in the rest of the water. When you've got a crystal on your finger, gently lower your finger into the glass of supercooled water and watch what happens.

5 How did that happen?

If everything has worked properly the water should instantly start to solidify, with ice crystals spreading through the water to make ice. If you want to skip this step you can always just leave the water inside its plastic bottle and hit it on the side to kick-start the process. That one small movement is all that's needed to start a chain reaction through all the molecules in the water!

SUMMARY

Tap water will usually freeze at 0°C because of the chemicals and impurities in the water. The molecules can latch onto these impurities, and freezing is simple. In purified water there are no impurities, so if you're careful the water can be cooled to well below its normal freezing point.

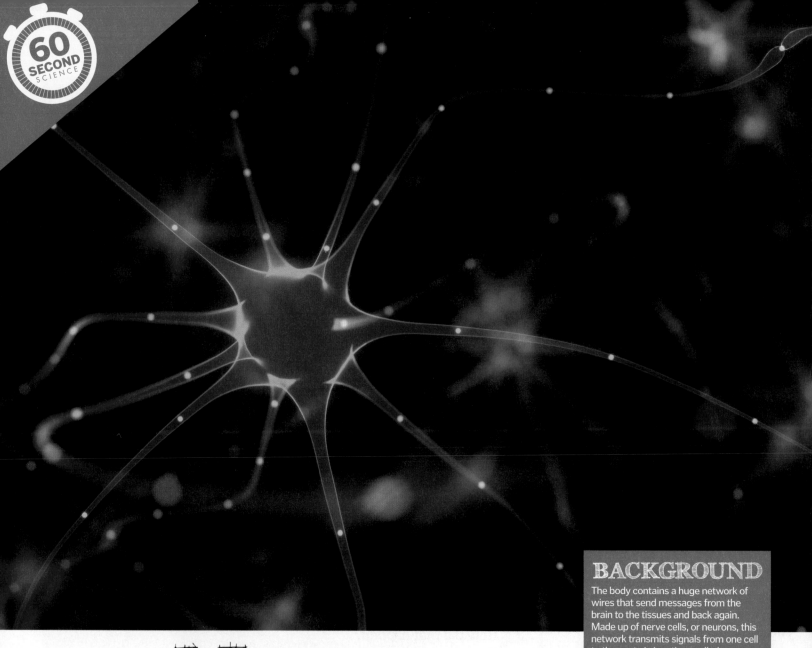

Nerve signals

DIG INTO THE BIOLOGICAL WIRES THAT SEND MESSAGES AROUND YOUR BODY

Electrical signals travel through nerve cells as impulses called action potentials. When nerve cells are at rest, their membranes have a charge difference on the inside compared to the outside. This happens because pumps in the nerve cell membrane push ions in and out of the cell. Ions have a charge, and the membrane is an insulator, so together they work a bit like a battery. The outside of the nerve cell has a positive charge compared to the inside, creating an electrical potential. When the nerve receives a message, it opens channels in the membrane that allow ions to move across. Ions sitting outside the cell rush in, and the inside of the membrane rapidly becomes positively charged. The current created by the moving ions opens more channels further along the nerve, and the impulse starts to travel along as a wave. Behind it, the channels snap shut, allowing the membrane to reset.

BACKGROUND

The body contains a huge network of wires that send messages from the brain to the tissues and back again. Made up of nerve cells, or neurons, this network transmits signals from one cell to the next via junctions called synapses. Neurons process dozens of incoming chemical signals, before deciding whether to pass the information on. To send a message to the next cell in the network, they trigger lightning-fast waves of electrical activity.

INSIDE AXONS

Human nerve cells are small and thin, so to get to grips with how these biological wires work, scientists turned to something bigger. A type of squid called Loligo has a giant axon that travels down the whole length of its body, sending messages from head to tail. It's only one cell, but it measures a full millimetre across, allowing scientists to poke electrodes inside its membrane to find out how it works.

The two scientists who made it famous were Alan Hodgkin and Andrew Huxley who performed experiments in 1939. Using electrodes, they found out that when an action potential fires, the voltage inside of the cell becomes 40-50 mV higher than the outside. Their research to uncover the inner workings of an action potential later earned them the Nobel Prize for Physiology or Medicine in 1963.

ANATOMY OF A NERVE CELL

These crucial components allow neurons to pass messages around the body

"Ions have a charge, and the nerve membrane is an insulator, so together they work a bit like a battery"

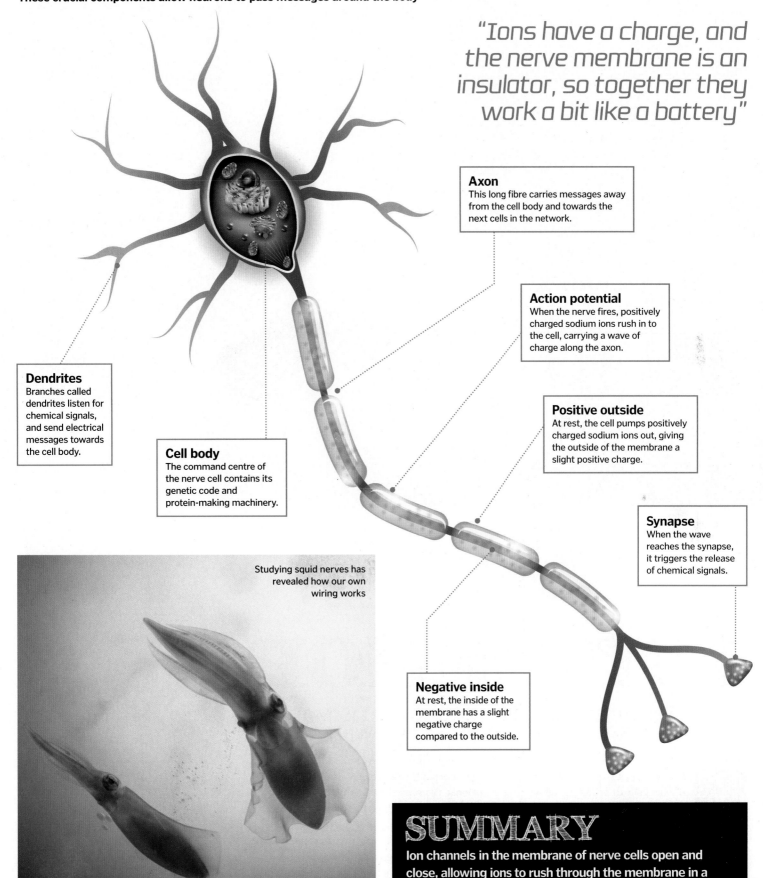

Axon
This long fibre carries messages away from the cell body and towards the next cells in the network.

Action potential
When the nerve fires, positively charged sodium ions rush in to the cell, carrying a wave of charge along the axon.

Positive outside
At rest, the cell pumps positively charged sodium ions out, giving the outside of the membrane a slight positive charge.

Dendrites
Branches called dendrites listen for chemical signals, and send electrical messages towards the cell body.

Cell body
The command centre of the nerve cell contains its genetic code and protein-making machinery.

Synapse
When the wave reaches the synapse, it triggers the release of chemical signals.

Negative inside
At rest, the inside of the membrane has a slight negative charge compared to the outside.

Studying squid nerves has revealed how our own wiring works

SUMMARY
Ion channels in the membrane of nerve cells open and close, allowing ions to rush through the membrane in a travelling wave. This sends electrical signals pulsing along the axon.

© Getty

Star formation

EVERYTHING YOU SEE AROUND YOU IS MADE OF STARDUST, INCLUDING YOUR OWN BODY

Every star in the universe starts life as a cloud of gas called a nebula. Gravitational forces pull the gas particles together, forming clumps that steadily grow in size. As more gas joins the cluster, gravity intensifies, the pressure starts to build, and the temperature rises. When the gas is hot enough, the star bursts into life and the atoms inside start to smash together, joining to become heavier elements. This process of nuclear fusion releases energy that warms the star even further. As gravity pulls the star inwards, the exploding gases pushes outwards, holding these vast nuclear reactors together as hot, swirling balls of gas. But, as stars blaze through their fuel supplies, this delicate balance starts to destabilise. They first expand, sometimes even explode, and then, when their fuel runs out, they collapse.

BACKGROUND

Stars are the great engines of the universe. Raging at temperatures above 15 million degrees, their insides swirl with a plasma soup of subatomic particles. The gravitational pull inside is so intense that it squashes atoms together. These blazing nuclear reactions forge heavier elements, radiating energy in the process. When the most massive stars die, they spill these elements out in supernova blasts, creating clouds of gas and dust that give birth to even more stars.

HEAVY ELEMENTS

At the start of the universe, the only element that existed was hydrogen. All the other elements in the periodic table came from stars. Different stars form different combinations of elements; many make only helium, but massive stars keep combining atoms to forge elements as heavy as iron.

However, once a star has started to make iron, it's in trouble. Making heavier elements uses more energy than it produces, so the star can't make enough outwards force to hold off the pull of gravity. The core collapses, the star explodes, and this releases a burst of energy that can fuse iron and other elements. Heavy elements produced in the explosion burst out into space, where they make their way into the dust clouds that produce the next generation of stars and planets.

THE LIFE CYCLE OF A STAR

The path a star follows from birth to death depends on its mass

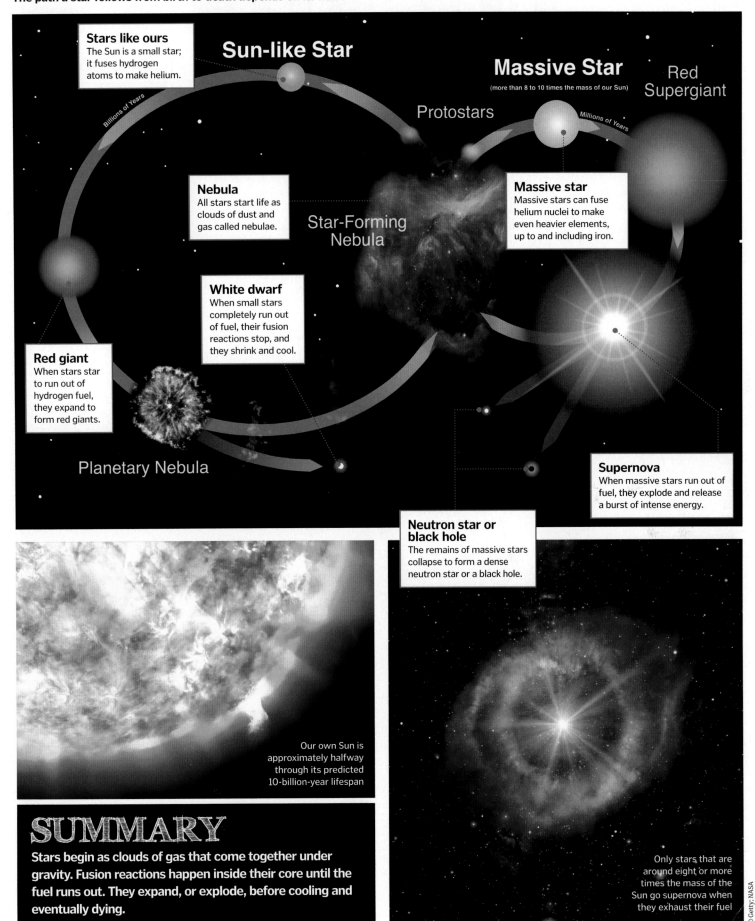

Stars like ours
The Sun is a small star; it fuses hydrogen atoms to make helium.

Sun-like Star

Massive Star
(more than 8 to 10 times the mass of our Sun)

Red Supergiant

Protostars

Billions of Years

Millions of Years

Nebula
All stars start life as clouds of dust and gas called nebulae.

Star-Forming Nebula

Massive star
Massive stars can fuse helium nuclei to make even heavier elements, up to and including iron.

White dwarf
When small stars completely run out of fuel, their fusion reactions stop, and they shrink and cool.

Red giant
When stars star to run out of hydrogen fuel, they expand to form red giants.

Planetary Nebula

Supernova
When massive stars run out of fuel, they explode and release a burst of intense energy.

Neutron star or black hole
The remains of massive stars collapse to form a dense neutron star or a black hole.

Our own Sun is approximately halfway through its predicted 10-billion-year lifespan

Only stars that are around eight or more times the mass of the Sun go supernova when they exhaust their fuel

SUMMARY

Stars begin as clouds of gas that come together under gravity. Fusion reactions happen inside their core until the fuel runs out. They expand, or explode, before cooling and eventually dying.

© Getty; NASA

Fossils

DISCOVER LIFE FORMS THAT LIVED MILLIONS OR BILLIONS OF YEARS AGO BEFORE BEING TURNED TO STONE

Mention fossils and many people think instantly of dinosaurs. These huge reptiles may have left some of the largest, most impressive fossils, but they are not nearly the oldest. The world of fossils is a varied one encompassing wonders as extraordinary as trilobites, large woodlouse-like creatures that crawled on the bed of tropical seas; brightly coloured petrified wood from long lost forests in Arizona; and coprolite which are fossilised animal droppings.

The study of fossils dates back to ancient times. In the fifth century BCE, Greek philosopher Xenophanes discovered the fossils of sea creatures and recognised what they were. From this he was able to say with confidence that the sea once covered what was then dry land.

Studying fossils helps us learn more about the history of life on Earth. For example, unearthing the Archaeopteryx and other similar specimens helped scientists piece together the evolutionary links between dinosaurs and birds.

BACKGROUND

A fossil was a living organism which, following its death, turned to stone.

If an organism dies under specific conditions, the soft tissues decay to leave the skeleton which gets buried by many layers of sediment. Over millions of years, the bones get dissolved by mineral-rich water and the minerals fill the space where the skeleton was to leave a rock replica.

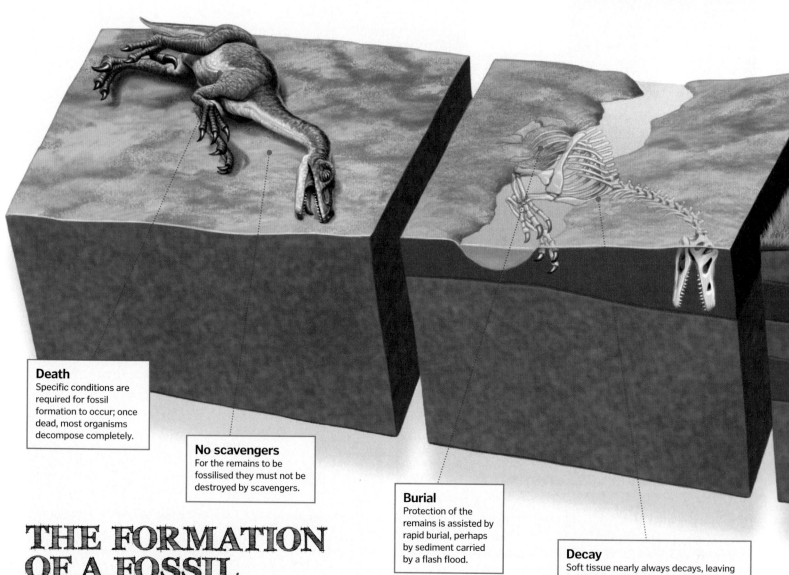

Death
Specific conditions are required for fossil formation to occur; once dead, most organisms decompose completely.

No scavengers
For the remains to be fossilised they must not be destroyed by scavengers.

Burial
Protection of the remains is assisted by rapid burial, perhaps by sediment carried by a flash flood.

Decay
Soft tissue nearly always decays, leaving only harder material such as bones to fossilise, although creatures with exoskeletons can fossilise completely.

THE FORMATION OF A FOSSIL

How a living organism can be turned into stone and preserved for millions of years

TOP FIVE FOSSIL DISCOVERIES

The oldest
In 2017 scientists discovered fossils of microscopic tube-like bacteria structures, found in Canada. They are about 4.2 billion years old and grew around deep-sea vents.

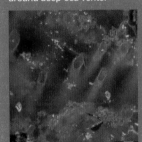

The largest
Fossilised bones from Argentina represent the largest known dinosaur. Patagotitan mayorum was nearly 40m long and weighed over 70 tons.

The smallest
Not all fossils are massive; some are so small you need a microscope to see them. Marine microfossils known as Chitinozoa, for example, can be as little as 0.05mm long.

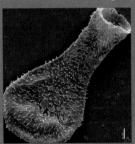

The rarest
Soft tissue usually decays before fossilising, so fossils of creatures with no hard parts are rare. However, researchers at Berlin Free University recently found octopus fossils.

The family tree
Hominin fossils, such as the famous Lucy specimen, have enabled scientists to study human evolution. These findings have helped to shed light on our ancient cousins.

Deeper burial
Over time, geological events deposit more sediment, so the remains become buried to ever-greater depths.

Exposure
Although they form deep in the Earth, fossils can be exposed due to geological processes such as erosion or uplift.

Discovery
Once exposed, fossils can be discovered by palaeontologists, who painstakingly extract them from the surrounding rock.

> "Dinosaurs may have left some of the largest, most impressive fossils, but they are not nearly the oldest"

Lithification
Compaction solidifies the sedimentary material in a process called lithification. The biological remnants are now encased in solid rock.

Permineralisation
Mineral-laden water seeps through the rock, filling pores in biological material with minerals, turning them into rock.

Make your own fossils

CREATE SOME FAKE FOSSILS – BUT DON'T WORRY, THESE WON'T TAKE AS LONG AS THE REAL THING!

1 Plaster of Paris

To create these fossils you will need some plaster of Paris, water, modelling clay, a shallow bowl, a seashell, paints and a paintbrush.

First, you'll need to mix up the plaster of Paris with water to make a thick liquid. This will form your fossil, but you need to make it slightly thicker than the packet will likely recommend. Combine one cup of plaster of Paris and one cup of water, then mix them together to create a smooth mixture. When left to set over a few hours the plaster will harden, so before that happens you need to make your fossil shape.

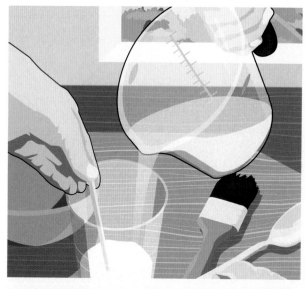

2 Shell shaped

To create your fossil imprint you'll need your shell from the beach, or another interesting item with a good texture. Try to choose something that will look like it could have been encased in rock millions of years ago.

To make your mold, fill the bowl to around two centimetres deep with modelling clay. Press it down with your fingers to make sure it's flat and there are no gaps.

3 Press it in

Push the shell (or other chosen item) into the clay firmly and leave it there for a few seconds, then carefully take it out. Millions of years ago, dinosaurs would stand in soft clay like this, leaving a footprint. If the water level rose, soft mud would fill this print, which would be compressed over time as more and more mud layered on top of it over thousands of years.

Experiment with different shell shapes to create a variety of interesting fossils

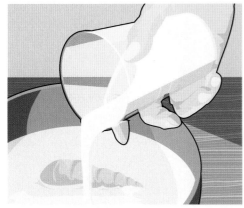

4 Pour and set

To simulate the soft mud, you need to pour the plaster of Paris into the mold that you created in the clay. You'll need to leave it for at least 12 hours so it can set and go really hard. Remember, if this were a real fossil, the process would take thousands of years as the pressure of mud and soil pressed down on the footprint and eventually transformed the mud into hard rock.

5 Paint it!

When your plaster is set, carefully ease it away from the clay. You might need to ask an adult to do this with a knife if you can't get it out by hand. Now you can paint your fossil pale brown, grey or cream, and paint the space around it in a darker shade, to make it look like the real thing. Try burying your finished fossil in sand and challenge your friends to find it, just like real fossil hunters!

"To create your fossil shape you'll need a shell from the beach"

SUMMARY

If you find a shell-like fossil in rocks at the beach, it's possible that you've found a trilobite. These sea creatures had hard shells covering their outer layer, but their insides were soft. After they died, these soft inner parts decayed and minerals filled the space inside them, eventually hardening into fossils over millions of years.

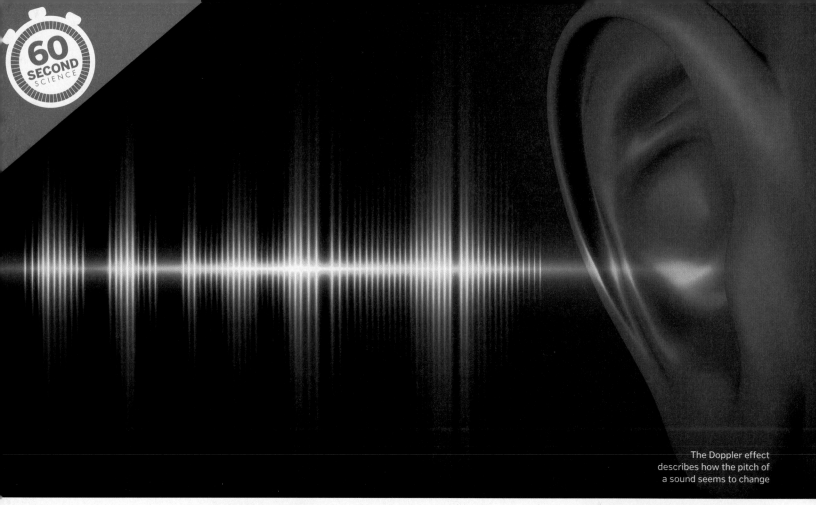

The Doppler effect describes how the pitch of a sound seems to change

The Doppler effect

HOW SOUND AND LIGHT WAVES CHANGE AS THEY MOVE TOWARDS OR AWAY FROM US

We are all familiar with the way a siren seems to change as an ambulance rushes past. The pitch of an approaching siren will increase, then decrease again as the vehicle speeds away.

This is known as the Doppler effect, and is caused by sound waves effectively bunching together or stretching out depending on the relative motion of the source of the sound and the person who hears it.

The pitch that you hear is determined by the sound's frequency, or the number of waves per second. The siren's frequency doesn't change, but as the ambulance travels towards you, the same number of waves are compressed into a decreasing distance. This increases the frequency of the sound waves you hear, so the pitch seems higher. As the ambulance travels away, the sound waves are spread across a growing distance, reducing the frequency you hear so the pitch seems lower.

BACKGROUND

In the early 1840s, Austrian physicist Christian Doppler was the first to describe how sound and light waves seem to change as the distance between the source and an observer is increasing or decreasing.

The theory was tested in 1845 by Christoph Buys Ballot. In his experiment, he asked musicians to play a constant note while on a moving train cart. The note he heard from the platform changed as the train sped past.

LIGHT SHIFT

The principle of the Doppler effect applies to light as well as sound. The frequency of a light wave indicates its colour, so by studying how the light of a moving object changes, it is possible to determine whether it is moving towards or away from us.

This is the method that American astronomer Edwin Hubble used to conclude that most galaxies are moving away from our own, therefore the universe must be expanding. The light from most cosmic objects is shifted towards the lower-frequency, red end of the visible light spectrum. The light from some stars and galaxies is shifted towards the blue end of the spectrum, implying they are moving towards us.

"The sound waves effectively bunch up or stretch out"

DOPPLER IN ACTION

How sound and light waves change as they move towards or away from us

Driving towards
As the ambulance travels towards the observer, the waves are compressed into a smaller distance.

Siren
The siren blares at a constant frequency. To the ambulance driver, the pitch of the siren remains the same.

Driving away
As the ambulance travels away, the same number of waves are spread over a larger distance.

Observer 1
The apparent increase in wavelength and decrease in frequency is heard as a lower pitched siren.

Observer 2
To this observer, the siren's frequency appears to increase and its wavelength decrease, giving the impression of a higher pitch.

Austrian physicist Christian Doppler (1803-1853) first described the effect that is now named after him

Sirens are an everyday example of the Doppler effect in action

SUMMARY

A sound's apparent pitch is relative to the changing distance between the noise source and the observer. Decreasing distances result in a higher pitch and increasing distances result in a lower pitch.

© Getty; Highway Patrol Images

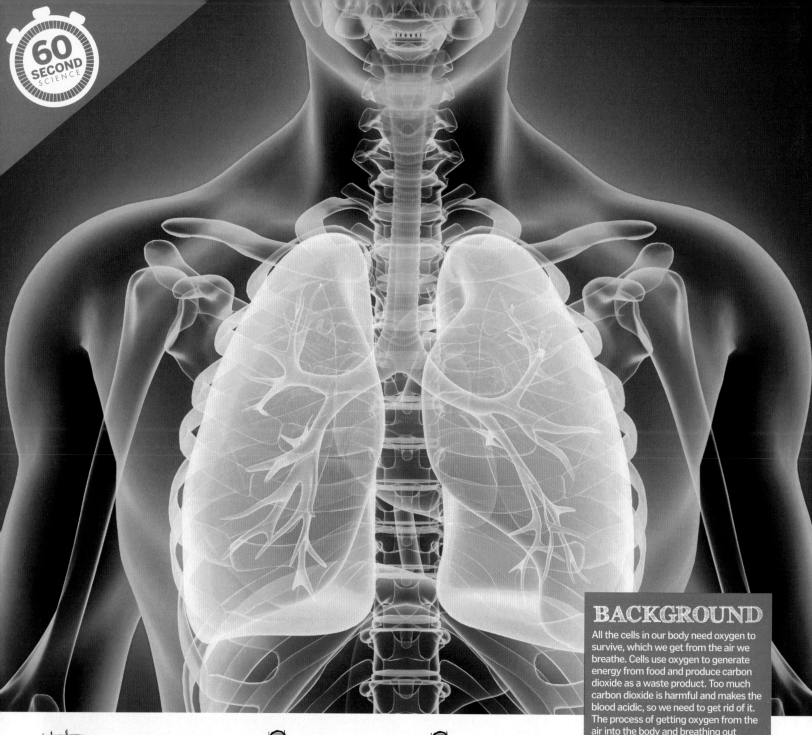

Respiration

DISCOVER THE SCIENCE BEHIND EVERY BREATH YOU TAKE

 Oxygen's journey into our cells starts with breathing, which is controlled by a part of the brain called the respiratory centre. It sends signals to the intercostal muscles and the diaphragm, telling them to contract, expanding the lungs and pulling air down the windpipe and into the branching tubes of the lungs. Each tube ends in balloon-like sacs called alveoli, which are surrounded by tiny blood vessels.

The air that we inhale is approximately 21 per cent oxygen but there's a lower level in the bloodstream because some of it gets used up by our cells. Similarly, air contains less than 0.05 per cent carbon dioxide, but there's a higher level in the blood because it is produced by our cells as a waste product. Due to these different concentrations, oxygen passes from the alveoli into the blood – through the process of diffusion – while carbon dioxide moves the other way.

BACKGROUND

All the cells in our body need oxygen to survive, which we get from the air we breathe. Cells use oxygen to generate energy from food and produce carbon dioxide as a waste product. Too much carbon dioxide is harmful and makes the blood acidic, so we need to get rid of it. The process of getting oxygen from the air into the body and breathing out unwanted carbon dioxide in return is known as respiration.

AEROBIC OR ANAEROBIC

We need to respire constantly so that our cells can generate energy and power every function in the body. To avoid there ever being a lapse, there are two types of respiration. Aerobic respiration requires oxygen, producing carbon dioxide and water as waste products. An alternative 'back-up' process called anaerobic respiration happens when oxygen isn't available, but it creates a chemical called lactic acid. If lactic acid builds up in cells and tissues it can be toxic, and causes a burning feeling in our muscles during and after intense exercise. As a result, we can't rely on anaerobic respiration for too long, explaining why you can't run a marathon at sprinting speed.

BREATHE IN, BREATHE OUT

From air to blood – how oxygen gets into the body

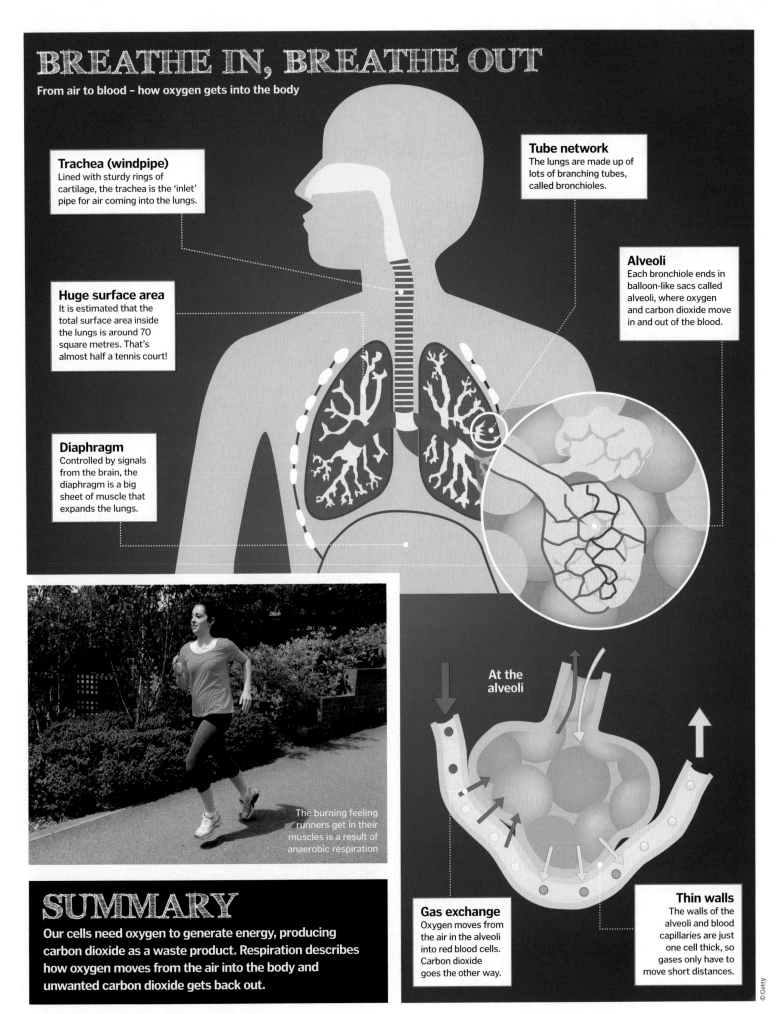

Trachea (windpipe)
Lined with sturdy rings of cartilage, the trachea is the 'inlet' pipe for air coming into the lungs.

Huge surface area
It is estimated that the total surface area inside the lungs is around 70 square metres. That's almost half a tennis court!

Diaphragm
Controlled by signals from the brain, the diaphragm is a big sheet of muscle that expands the lungs.

Tube network
The lungs are made up of lots of branching tubes, called bronchioles.

Alveoli
Each bronchiole ends in balloon-like sacs called alveoli, where oxygen and carbon dioxide move in and out of the blood.

The burning feeling runners get in their muscles is a result of anaerobic respiration

At the alveoli

Gas exchange
Oxygen moves from the air in the alveoli into red blood cells. Carbon dioxide goes the other way.

Thin walls
The walls of the alveoli and blood capillaries are just one cell thick, so gases only have to move short distances.

SUMMARY

Our cells need oxygen to generate energy, producing carbon dioxide as a waste product. Respiration describes how oxygen moves from the air into the body and unwanted carbon dioxide gets back out.

© Getty

Build a lung

TURN EVERYDAY HOUSEHOLD ITEMS INTO A WORKING LUNG MODEL

1 Cut your bottle

For this experiment you will need a two-litre plastic bottle, a plastic shopping bag (or sheet of similarly thin and strong plastic), scissors, a rubber band, a balloon, a drinking straw, some modelling clay and sticky tape.

With the help of an adult, cut the bottle in half. Discard the bottom half and the lid as you will only need the top half for this experiment. Cut a square of plastic from the shopping bag and make sure it is big enough to cover the bottom of the cut bottle with room to spare. The edges don't need to be perfectly straight so don't worry about being too neat.

2 Secure your plastic sheet

Stand the bottle on its top, and place your cut plastic over the large, open end. With the help of a rubber band, secure your cut plastic around the bottle. Carefully pull the edges, so that a taught surface is formed across the top. Once you are happy with this, you can trim off the excess plastic. This represents your diaphragm, the muscle that contracts and relaxes, forcing your lungs to fill with air and then empty.

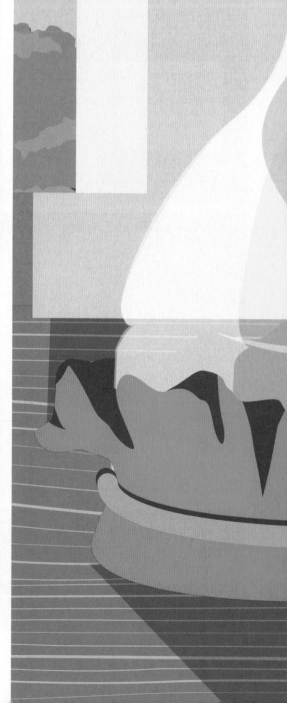

In this simple model the balloon behaves like a miniature lung

3 Build your breathing mechanism

You are now ready to add your breathing mechanism. Place a straw inside a balloon, which will act as a lung. Next, secure the straw in place with plenty of tape, as this seal will need to be airtight. Now test the seal by blowing into the straw; if the balloon doesn't inflate slightly then the seal needs to be improved by being tightened up some more.

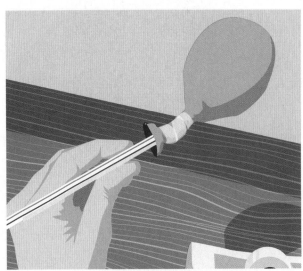

4 Install your lung

Drop the balloon end into the bottle's opening. This needs to be secured in place, which can be achieved using modelling clay. Press the modelling clay down firmly to create a seal, which must be completely airtight just like we did with our tape and straw in Step 3. The model won't work if air is able to enter the bottle by any other means than the straw.

5 Complete your model

The final step is to add a means of moving the plastic sheet up and down. Adding a sticky tape 'tab' to the bottom of the plastic will achieve this. Take a piece of tape and fold it in half like a curved 'V' shape, so that the sticky sides are together and the ends are left exposed. Stick the exposed ends onto the middle of the plastic sheet securely, so that it can be pulled without coming off.

Once secure, gently pull and push the tab and see how the balloon 'lung' inflates and deflates.

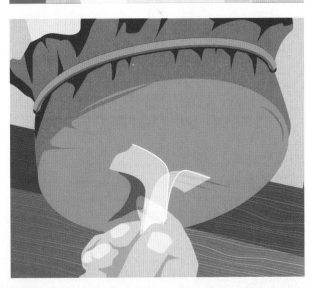

SUMMARY

This experiment cleverly illustrates how we breathe with simple household objects. When the diaphragm contracts in our bodies, air is able to enter the lungs due to the extra room this creates. When you exhale however, the diaphragm relaxes, forcing air out of your lungs. This is shown when you pull down and push up on the model's plastic sheet.

Special relativity

WHAT HAPPENS WHEN OBJECTS APPROACH THE SPEED OF LIGHT DEPENDS ON HOW YOU LOOK

According to Isaac Newton, an object in motion tends to stay in motion, force equals mass times acceleration, and for every action, there is an equal and opposite reaction. However, this physics doesn't work as you approach the speed of light.

If you were in a car and another car was travelling beside you at the same speed, it would look as though that car wasn't moving at all. But, Einstein thought, if you were travelling on a beam of light, a beam of light next to you wouldn't look as though it had stopped. It doesn't matter where you are, or how fast you're travelling, light moving through a vacuum always moves at the speed of light.

To make this possible, space and time have to change. To an outside observer, objects become shorter in the direction they are moving (space compresses). And, as things get faster, an observer sees time move more slowly (time dilates).

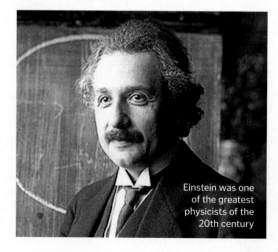

Einstein was one of the greatest physicists of the 20th century

BACKGROUND

Often written as c, the speed of light is a constant. It's the speed limit of the universe, and our understanding of physics depends on the fact that nothing can break through it. Electromagnetic radiation is the only thing that can reach maximum pace, topping out at 299,792,458 meters per second in a vacuum. When anything with mass tries to approach full speed, strange things happen to space and time. Einstein explained them using special relativity.

ALBERT EINSTEIN

Einstein lived between 1879 and 1955 and, during that time, he made some monumental contributions to physics. He grew up in Germany, fascinated by physical forces and the mysteries of geometry, but he ran away from school at the age of 16. He managed to get into a university in Switzerland without any high school qualifications, and he started his working life in a patent office.

All the while, he had been pondering the theories of physicist, James Clerk Maxwell, and thinking about the movement of beams of light. In 1905, he shared his thoughts with the world. In the space of one year, he published his theory of special relativity, a paper about light and quantum theory, another paper to prove that atoms existed, and his famous equation $E=mc^2$.

SPECIAL RELATIVITY MADE SIMPLE

This thought experiment explains the fundamental concepts behind Einstein's theory

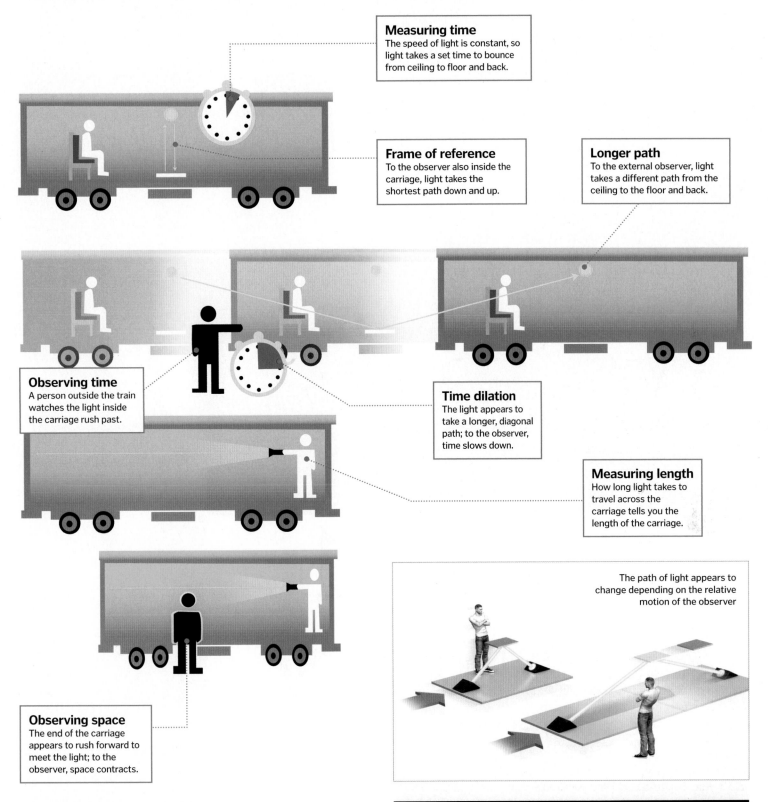

Measuring time
The speed of light is constant, so light takes a set time to bounce from ceiling to floor and back.

Frame of reference
To the observer also inside the carriage, light takes the shortest path down and up.

Longer path
To the external observer, light takes a different path from the ceiling to the floor and back.

Observing time
A person outside the train watches the light inside the carriage rush past.

Time dilation
The light appears to take a longer, diagonal path; to the observer, time slows down.

Measuring length
How long light takes to travel across the carriage tells you the length of the carriage.

Observing space
The end of the carriage appears to rush forward to meet the light; to the observer, space contracts.

The path of light appears to change depending on the relative motion of the observer

"It doesn't matter where you are, or how fast you're travelling, light moving through a vacuum always moves at the speed of light"

SUMMARY

Special relativity describes how, as objects approach the speed of light, time dilates and space compresses. But you only see it happening if you observe from the outside the system.

© Getty

General relativity

GET TO GRIPS WITH EINSTEIN'S THEORY OF THE UNIVERSE

According to Isaac Newton's first law of motion, objects do not accelerate unless an external force acts upon them. However, Einstein realised that when you are in freefall, you feel weightless, so you feel no force even though you're accelerating towards the ground.

He determined that what we experience as gravity must be the result of massive objects curving space-time itself. Any objects moving through this warped space-time follow as short a path as possible, which is a curve. This helped to prove that Earth's orbit was not determined by gravity pulling it towards the Sun, as had been previously thought, but was rather the result of curved space-time forcing our planet along the shortest possible route around its host star.

BACKGROUND

In 1905, Albert Einstein published his theory of special relativity, explaining that the speed of light in a vacuum is constant and so are the laws of physics when they are observed while not accelerating. He proved that everything moves relative to everything else, but it only applied to special cases; it did not apply to observers who were speeding up or slowing down. Einstein set about extending his theory so that it could apply to everything in the universe, forming a theory of general relativity.

RELATIVITY'S LEGACY

Einstein had solved the mystery of where gravity comes from – the curving of space-time. It was discovered that the curvature of space-time around extremely dense objects is infinite, forming a hole in the fabric of space-time, known as a black hole.

Using general relativity, Einstein proved that gravity bends the path of light and gives stars a false position in the sky when seen from Earth.

The equations of general relativity helped reveal that the universe is expanding, leading to the development of the Big Bang theory.

BENDING SPACE-TIME

Explaining motion and the path of light in space

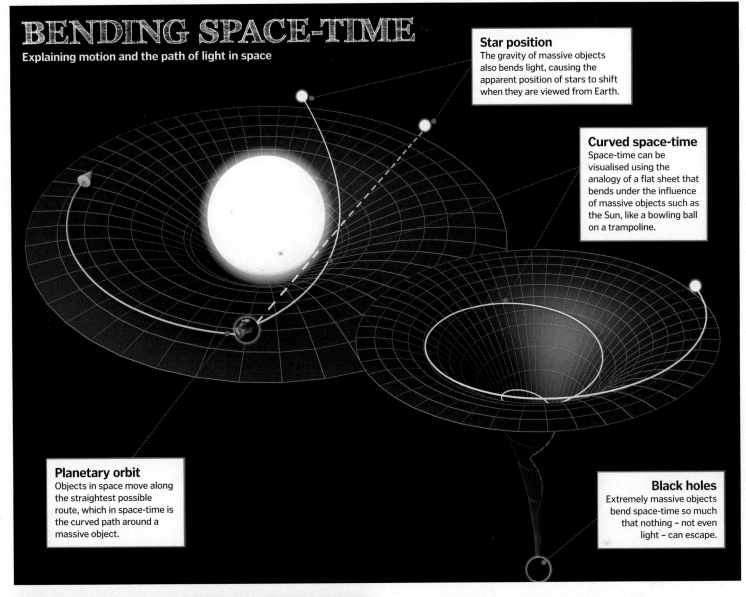

Star position
The gravity of massive objects also bends light, causing the apparent position of stars to shift when they are viewed from Earth.

Curved space-time
Space-time can be visualised using the analogy of a flat sheet that bends under the influence of massive objects such as the Sun, like a bowling ball on a trampoline.

Planetary orbit
Objects in space move along the straightest possible route, which in space-time is the curved path around a massive object.

Black holes
Extremely massive objects bend space-time so much that nothing – not even light – can escape.

Earth's gravity effectively bends the surrounding space-time like a bowling ball on a trampoline

SUMMARY

The theory of general relativity proves that gravity is caused by the curvature of space-time and does not pull objects, but instead forces them along the shortest possible path.

Albert Einstein
1879-1955

Einstein considered his general theory to be the culmination of his life's research. After it was published in 1915, he became world famous almost overnight and in 1921, was awarded the Nobel Prize for Physics. He published more than 300 scientific papers in his lifetime, changing the world's view on space, time and matter.

© Thinkstock; WIKI

Magnetism

WHY DOES OUR PLANET HAVE POLES, AND WHY DO OPPOSITES ATTRACT?

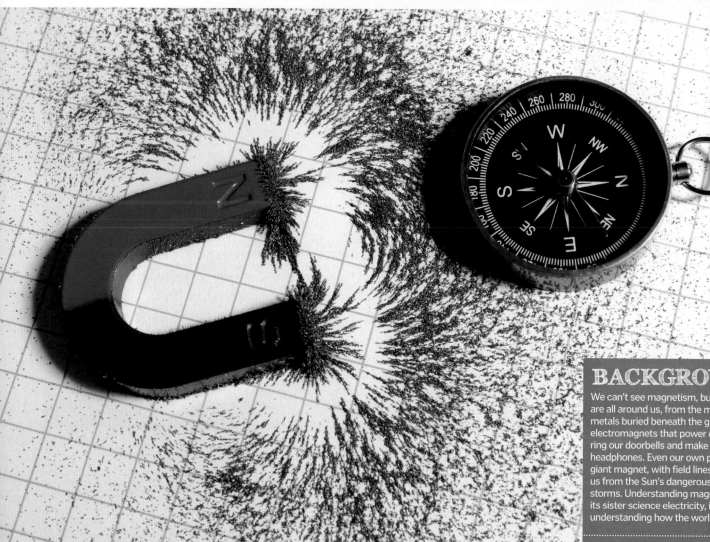

BACKGROUND

We can't see magnetism, but its effects are all around us, from the magnetic metals buried beneath the ground to the electromagnets that power our motors, ring our doorbells and make music in our headphones. Even our own planet is a giant magnet, with field lines that shield us from the Sun's dangerous particle storms. Understanding magnetism, and its sister science electricity, is crucial to understanding how the world works.

 The electrons around the outside of atoms each have a tiny negative charge. They race about in clouds around the atomic nucleus, spinning as they go. As they spin, they make a current, and it's the movement of this current that generates magnetism. If unpaired electrons spin in opposite directions, they cancel out each other's magnetism. But, if they spin together, their magnetic fields get stronger. These fields have a north and a south pole, surrounded by invisible magnetic field lines. When two fields come close together, opposite poles attract and like poles repel. Only three naturally occurring metals have this property: iron, nickel and cobalt. If enough electrons spin together, it can create a magnetic field so strong that nearby objects can feel it.

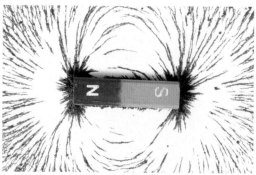

Sprinkle iron filings around a magnet to reveal the invisible field lines

VISUALISING FIELDS

Invisible magnetic field lines affect any magnetic materials that cross their path. We can feel and see their effects, but we can't see the lines themselves. One of the best ways to find their outline is to use iron filings.

Place a bar magnet on a white sheet of paper and sprinkle iron filings around the edges. The magnetic field will capture the tiny chips of magnetic metal, and they will line up along the field lines. You'll notice clusters at the poles, extending in arcs around the sides of the magnet. And, if you put more than one magnet together, you can see what happens when field lines interact. Watch the lines curve away as magnets repel, or pull together as they attract.

WHAT MAKES A MAGNET?

Discover what makes certain materials magnetic and how their invisible fields interact

Magnetic metal
Patches of unpaired electrons spin in the same direction, but these domains don't all line up.

Magnet
It all of the domains line up together, their magnetic effects combine to make an external magnetic field.

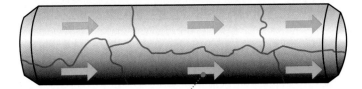

Making a magnet
Applying a strong magnetic field to a magnetic metal can pull the domains into alignment.

Field lines
A bar magnet on its own produces a pattern of field lines that curve from north to south.

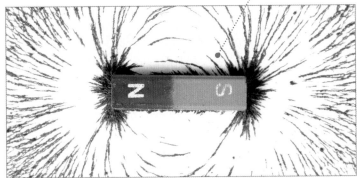

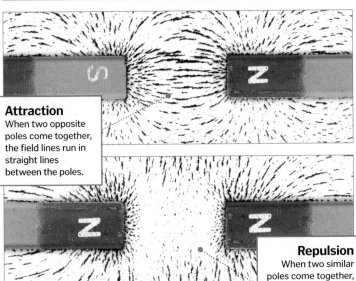

Attraction
When two opposite poles come together, the field lines run in straight lines between the poles.

Repulsion
When two similar poles come together, the field lines bend away from the poles.

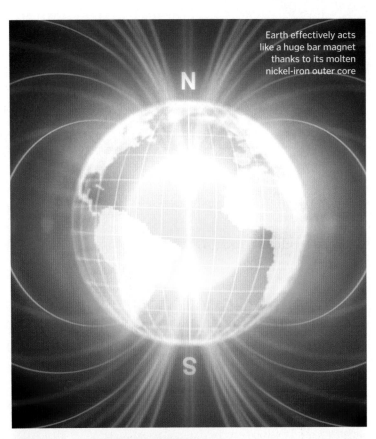

Earth effectively acts like a huge bar magnet thanks to its molten nickel-iron outer core

Auroras occur when our planet's magnetic field is bombarded by charged particles from the Sun

SUMMARY

Magnets have a north and a south pole and a magnetic field that attracts or repels electrons. Iron, nickel and cobalt are the only three metals that can be used to make permanent magnets.

© Getty

Make a compass

LEARN HOW TO FIND YOUR WAY NORTH
USING SIMPLE HOUSEHOLD OBJECTS AND
EARTH'S MAGNETIC FIELD

1 Assemble your tools

For this navigational experiment we'll firstly need a sewing needle, which is going to become the point of our compass. We'll also need a dish, water, some sticky tack or glue, a permanent marker pen and a magnet. A bar magnet will work best, but you can use a fridge magnet instead if you can't find one. A piece of stainless steel cutlery may work as well.

2 Magnetise the needle

Colour one end of your needle using the marker pen; this will help distinguish between north and south later. Next, magnetise the uncoloured end of the needle by stroking your magnet in one direction across the surface. Make sure to lift the magnet away with each new stroke. If you're using a bar magnet, you can choose which way the uncoloured end will point.

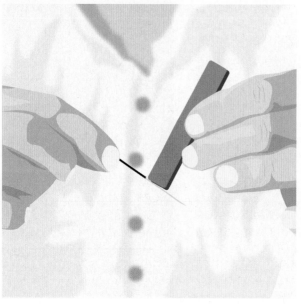

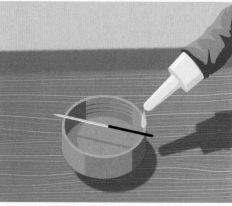

3 Attach a float

Now you've got yourself a magnetic needle, but it won't be able to rotate towards north or south until you place it on a surface where there's little friction; so the next task is to build one. Take the plastic bottle cap and place it upside-down on your work surface, then use the sticky tack or glue to securely attach the needle to the rim of the bottle cap.

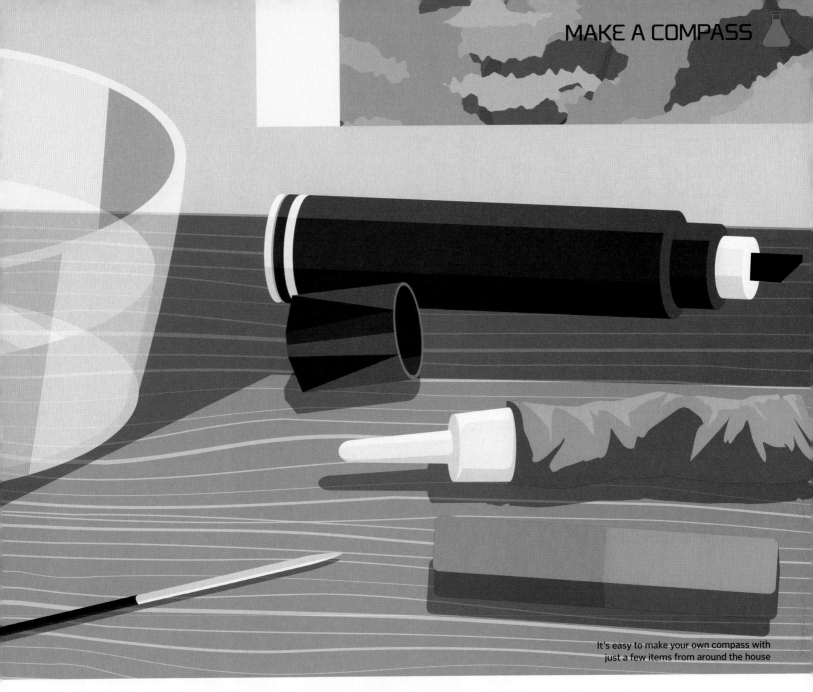

It's easy to make your own compass with just a few items from around the house

4 Add to water
Fill your dish with water to a depth of approximately two or three centimetres. Carefully place your compass on the water. As a liquid, water is an excellent choice for a low-friction surface. If Earth's magnetic field was stronger the needle could move on a solid surface, but when sat on water the needle will face little resistance when turning towards the poles.

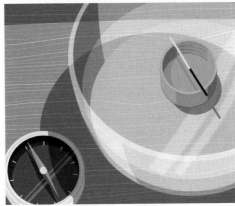

5 Find your orientation
As the water settles the needle will begin to turn and face the poles. Try gently spinning the compass; you should notice that the needle soon realigns itself to face the same direction as it did before you span it, just like any other compass. If you have a real compass or a smartphone with a compass app handy, you can now check to see which side of your needle is pointing north.

> "As the water settles the needle will begin to turn and face the poles"

SUMMARY
Metals that needles are made from (such as iron, nickel and cobalt) all have magnetic areas called domains. These usually point in different directions, but when exposed to a strong magnetic field they can briefly align and become magnetic. The needle tries to line up with the Earth's magnetosphere, generated by our planet's molten iron core.

How old is your body?

YOU WILL MAKE 2 MILLION NEW RED BLOOD CELLS IN THE TIME IT TAKES YOU TO READ THIS SENTENCE

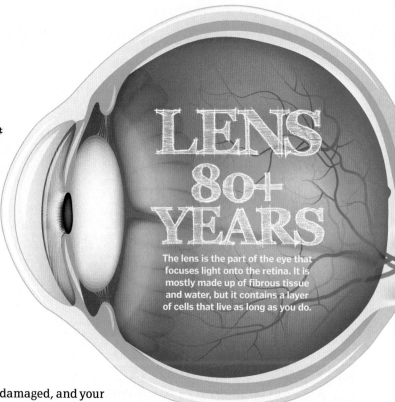

LENS 80+ YEARS

The lens is the part of the eye that focuses light onto the retina. It is mostly made up of fibrous tissue and water, but it contains a layer of cells that live as long as you do.

Your body contains 37.2 trillion cells. There are 86 billion neurons in your brain, 50 billion fat cells insulate your skin, and every cubic millimetre of your blood contains 4-6 million cells. But they don't live forever.

Cells get old and damaged, and your body is constantly racing to replace them. Red blood cells only live for about three months; 50 million skin cells flake away every day; and sperm cells only last for three to five days. Read on to find out just how old you really are.

CHEEK LINING
3 hours

Studies of cheek lining cells in saliva have revealed that the lining of the mouth might renew as fast as every 2.7 hours.

STOMACH LINING
2–9 days

A thick layer of mucus protects the cells lining the stomach, but they are still replaced at least once a week.

PLATELETS
10 days

Large cells called megakaryocytes make fragments called platelets, which plug leaks in blood vessels. They only last for around ten days.

EPIDERMAL CELLS
10–30 days

There are between 18 and 23 layers of dead cells on the outside of your skin. New cells push up from below the surface every few weeks.

SPERM 3–5 DAYS

Adult males produce fresh sperm constantly. These cells can survive for between three and five days as they search for an egg.

EGGS 50+ YEARS

Females are born with all of the egg cells they will ever have, but they are no longer released after the menopause.

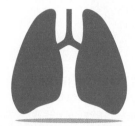

LUNG LINING 8 DAYS

The delicate lining of the lungs is just one cell thick and lasts just over a week.

CEREBRAL NEURONS 80+ YEARS

You might have heard that the whole body renews itself every seven years, but brain cells last as long as we do.

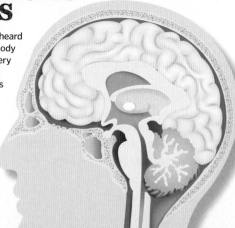

THE LIFESPAN OF YOUR CELLS

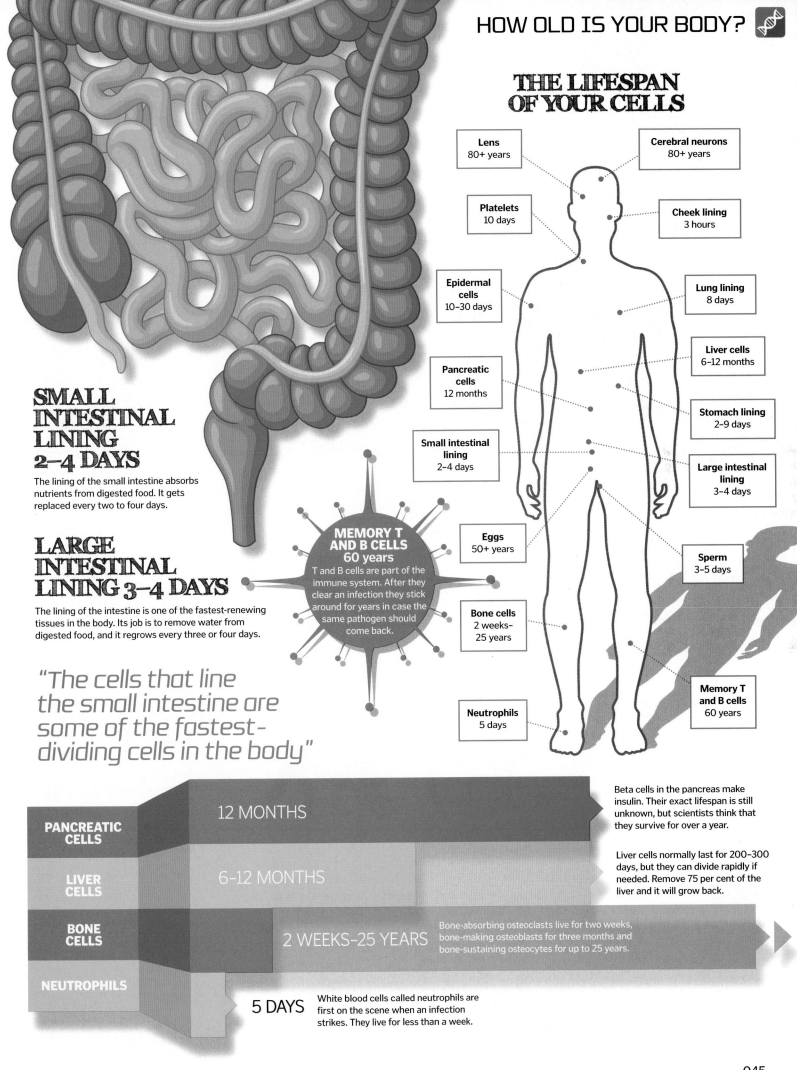

Lens
80+ years

Cerebral neurons
80+ years

Platelets
10 days

Cheek lining
3 hours

Epidermal cells
10–30 days

Lung lining
8 days

Pancreatic cells
12 months

Liver cells
6–12 months

Small intestinal lining
2–4 days

Stomach lining
2–9 days

Large intestinal lining
3–4 days

Eggs
50+ years

Sperm
3–5 days

Bone cells
2 weeks–25 years

Memory T and B cells
60 years

Neutrophils
5 days

MEMORY T AND B CELLS
60 years
T and B cells are part of the immune system. After they clear an infection they stick around for years in case the same pathogen should come back.

SMALL INTESTINAL LINING 2–4 DAYS

The lining of the small intestine absorbs nutrients from digested food. It gets replaced every two to four days.

LARGE INTESTINAL LINING 3–4 DAYS

The lining of the intestine is one of the fastest-renewing tissues in the body. Its job is to remove water from digested food, and it regrows every three or four days.

"The cells that line the small intestine are some of the fastest-dividing cells in the body"

PANCREATIC CELLS — 12 MONTHS

Beta cells in the pancreas make insulin. Their exact lifespan is still unknown, but scientists think that they survive for over a year.

LIVER CELLS — 6–12 MONTHS

Liver cells normally last for 200–300 days, but they can divide rapidly if needed. Remove 75 per cent of the liver and it will grow back.

BONE CELLS — 2 WEEKS–25 YEARS

Bone-absorbing osteoclasts live for two weeks, bone-making osteoblasts for three months and bone-sustaining osteocytes for up to 25 years.

NEUTROPHILS — 5 DAYS

White blood cells called neutrophils are first on the scene when an infection strikes. They live for less than a week.

Moments

GET STRAIGHT TO THE FACTS ABOUT THE SCIENCE OF PIVOTS AND LEVERS

Moments are turning forces, and you can find examples of them everywhere. Trying to undo a bolt with your fingers is almost impossible, but add a spanner and suddenly it becomes easy. This is because you're increasing the distance between the force and the pivot and therefore you're increasing the turning moment.

The same principle applies when using a screwdriver to pry open a can of syrup or paint, or closing the handles of a pair of scissors to slice through a sheet of card or a piece of string. The further away you apply the force from the pivot, the easier the task will become.

Moments don't have to be on opposite sides of the pivot, either. A heavy load in a wheelbarrow is close to the wheel, while the handles are further away. This means that you need less force in order to lift the contents. Understanding the simple principles of moments makes everyday tasks an awful lot easier to perform.

BACKGROUND

Moments come into play when forces act on an object that has a fixed point. For example, turning a door handle, sitting on a seesaw or closing a pair of scissors. When forces are applied to these objects they rotate around their fixed point, also known as the pivot or fulcrum. The 'moment' is the turning effect of the force. It tells us how much the object will rotate and in which direction. Put simply, a moment is a twist. It is also known as torque.

CALCULATING MOMENTS

To calculate a moment you need to know two things: the force (which is measured in Newtons) and the perpendicular distance between the pivot to the line of action of the force (which is measured in metres). When you multiply these two numbers you get the moment, which is measured in Newton metres (Nm).

For example, a seesaw has a pivot at the centre. If a person sits on one end, the moment can be calculated by taking the force of their weight on the seat and multiplying it by the distance from the seat to the middle of the seesaw.

Moments also have a direction, either clockwise or anticlockwise. When no one is sitting on the seesaw, the moments in both directions are equal. But when one person sits down the seesaw moves. If another person joins them by sitting on the other end, their body weight creates a moment in the opposite direction.

Moment (Nm) = Force (N) x distance (m)

MOMENTS IN ACTION

Take a trip to your local park to test turning moments for yourself

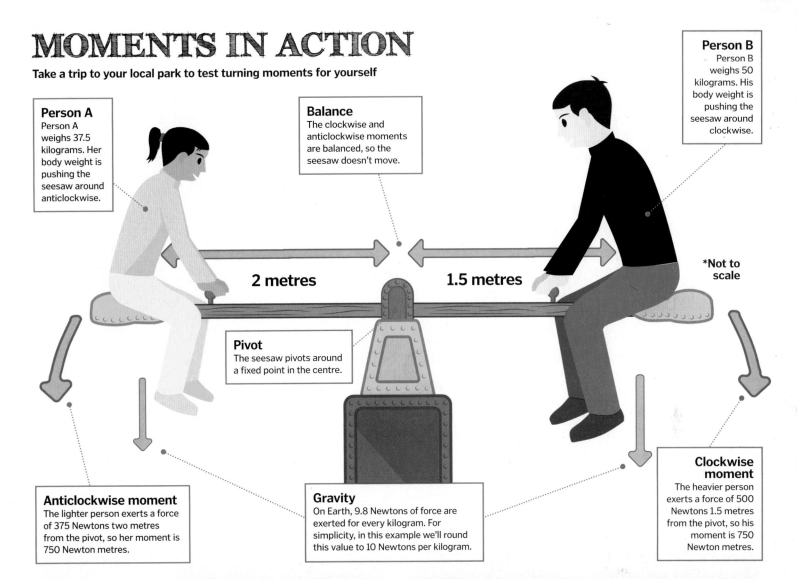

Person A
Person A weighs 37.5 kilograms. Her body weight is pushing the seesaw around anticlockwise.

Balance
The clockwise and anticlockwise moments are balanced, so the seesaw doesn't move.

Person B
Person B weighs 50 kilograms. His body weight is pushing the seesaw around clockwise.

2 metres

1.5 metres

*Not to scale

Pivot
The seesaw pivots around a fixed point in the centre.

Anticlockwise moment
The lighter person exerts a force of 375 Newtons two metres from the pivot, so her moment is 750 Newton metres.

Gravity
On Earth, 9.8 Newtons of force are exerted for every kilogram. For simplicity, in this example we'll round this value to 10 Newtons per kilogram.

Clockwise moment
The heavier person exerts a force of 500 Newtons 1.5 metres from the pivot, so his moment is 750 Newton metres.

Spanners make light work of bolts because they increase the distance between the pivot and the applied force

Greek mathematician Archimedes was one of the first people to explain how levers work

SUMMARY

Moments are the turning effects of forces. They have a direction, either clockwise or anticlockwise, and they can be calculated by multiplying the force exerted by its distance from the pivot.

Build a sturdy bridge

MAKE A BRIDGE THAT CAN TAKE THE WEIGHT OF A FEW BRICKS... WITH LOLLY STICKS!

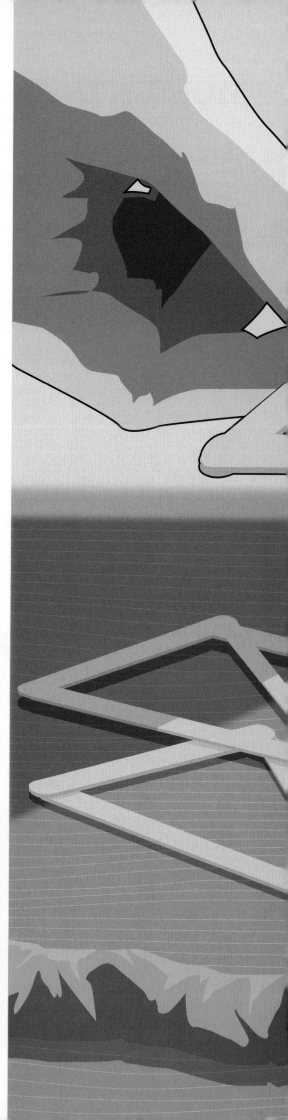

1 Make the sides

Start by making the sides of your bridge. Take three lolly sticks and stick them together in the shape of an equilateral triangle. Attach them with plenty of glue to make sure they're strong. Now attach another stick to the first, then add more sticks to make several triangles in a row, with more sticks at the top to strengthen them. Now repeat this process for the other side and leave them to dry.

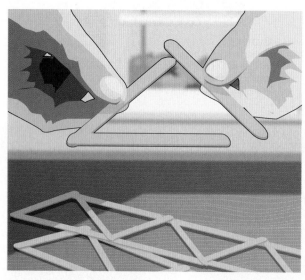

2 Create the base

For the base, stick several lolly sticks together in a line, then make another the same length. Use glue to attach more sticks across the two longer lines at right angles. Your base should look like a row of around four squares, and this should be the same length as your row of triangles. That's the main sections of your bridge finished, but before putting it together, we need to reinforce it.

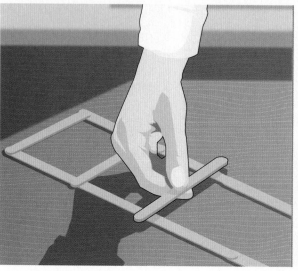

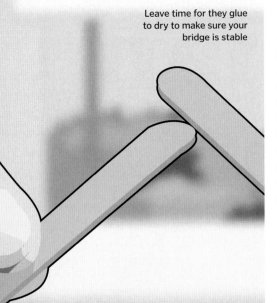

Leave time for they glue to dry to make sure your bridge is stable

3 Make it stronger

We're now going to add two more sticks inside each square. Use a dab of glue on the ends of each stick, but be sparing as you don't need to use too much. You should now have a base that looks like two long lines with a zigzag line running down the centre. You'll need to repeat this process again for the top of the bridge, but that will be slightly shorter than the base.

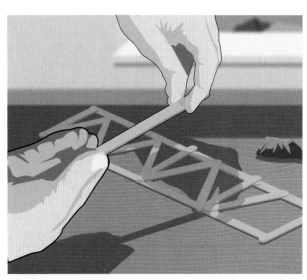

4 Attach the sides

This step can be a little bit awkward, but it's important. Hold one side of the bridge at a right-angle to the base, and using masking tape, attach the base to the side. You'll need to wrap the tape tightly around the two pieces to secure it. An extra pair of hands helps here, so ask a grown-up or a friend to help. Then do the same with the second side.

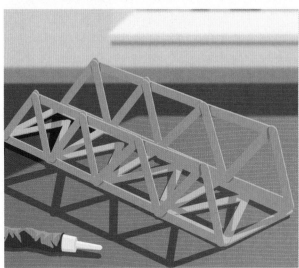

5 Top it off

You can now attach the top of your bridge with tape, just as you did with the base. Wait as long as you can to make sure the glue is set before you test it. Carefully put something heavy, like a brick, on the top of the bridge. It should support the weight – if it slips sideways, try adding more lolly sticks inside the bridge structure to make it even stronger.

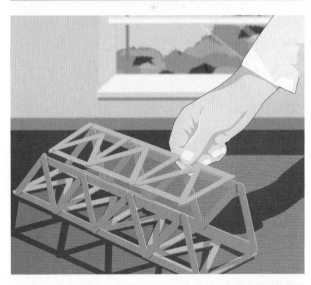

SUMMARY

Adding sticks at angles and attaching them strongly with glue helps to spread the weight placed on top of the bridge between all the sticks at the same time. If the sticks weren't attached, the structure would collapse. When the weight is added, some sticks are compressed while others are under tension, helping the bridge to withstand the pressure.

The human heartbeat

HOW ONE OF YOUR HARDEST-WORKING MUSCLES KEEPS YOUR BLOOD PUMPING

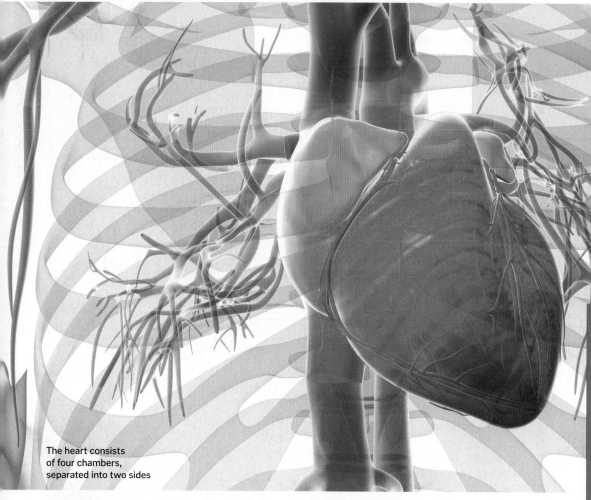

The heart consists of four chambers, separated into two sides

Your heart began to beat when you were a four-week-old foetus in the womb. Over the course of the average lifetime, it will beat over 2 billion times.

The heart is composed of four chambers separated into two sides. The right side receives deoxygenated blood from the body, and pumps it towards the lungs, where it picks up oxygen from the air you breathe. The oxygenated blood returns to the left side of the heart, where it is sent through the circulatory system, delivering oxygen and nutrients around the body.

The pumping action of the heart is coordinated by muscular contractions caused by electrical currents. The currents are generated from a patch of 'pacemaker' cells (see 'Fight or flight' boxout) that regularly trigger cardiac contractions known as systole. The upper chambers, or atria, which receive blood arriving at the heart, contract first. This forces blood to the lower, more muscular chambers, known as ventricles, which then contract to push blood out to the body. Following a brief stage where the heart tissue relaxes, known as diastole, the cycle starts over again.

FIGHT OR FLIGHT

A heartbeat begins at the sinoatrial node, a bundle of specialised cells in the right atrium. This acts as a natural pacemaker by generating an electrical current that moves throughout the heart, causing it to contract. When you are at rest, this happens between 60 to 100 times per minute on average. Under stressful situations however, such as an encounter with a predator, your brain will automatically trigger a 'fight or flight' response.

This results in the release of adrenaline and noradrenaline hormones that change the conductance of the sinoatrial node, increasing heart rate, and so providing the body with more available nutrients to either fight for survival or run for the hills.

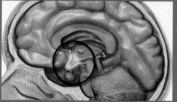

Adrenaline and noradrenaline secretion is governed by the hypothalamus

THE CARDIAC CYCLE

A single heartbeat is a series of organised steps that maximise blood-pumping efficiency

Right atrium
Deoxygenated blood from the rest of the body enters the chamber via the superior and inferior vena cava.

Left atrium
Oxygenated blood arrives from the lungs via the pulmonary vein and flows into this chamber.

Diastole
The cardiac muscle cells are relaxed, allowing blood to enter the ventricles freely.

Blood enters the atria
Circulated blood returns to the atrium to begin a new cycle.

Blood enters the ventricles
The blood moves down into the ventricular chamber due to a difference in pressure.

Semi-lunar valves open
The pressure in the chambers forces blood through the valves and into the aorta and pulmonary artery.

Atrial systole
The atria contract, decreasing in volume and squeezing blood through to the ventricles.

Ventricular systole
The ventricles contract, increasing pressure as the volume of the chambers decreases. The more muscular tissue of the ventricles allows blood to be pumped at a higher pressure than the atria.

Atrial diastole
The electrical current moves past the atria and the muscles relax.

Ventricular septum
A thick, muscular wall separates the two ventricular chambers of the heart.

SUMMARY

A complex arrangement of muscular chambers, valves and electrical currents ensure that your heart keeps beating and blood is continuously circulated around your body in the right direction.

"Over the course of the average lifetime, the heart will beat over 2 billion times"

Photosynthesis

OUR QUICK-FIRE GUIDE TO HOW PLANTS CAPTURE ENERGY FROM THE SUN

BACKGROUND

Using the Sun's energy, plants and other organisms can transform carbon dioxide and water into a sugar called glucose, which is then used for respiration. Oxygen is a by-product of this process, which is known as photosynthesis.

KEY FACTORS

The speed of photosynthesis is affected by three main factors: the amount of light, the amount of carbon dioxide and the temperature.

If there's too little of either of the key ingredients – light and carbon dioxide – photosynthesis slows down. However, if the Sun is too bright and too much light reaches the leaves, the pigments can become damaged.

Capturing light from the Sun doesn't rely on temperature, but using the stored energy to build sugar molecules does. This part of the process is done by molecular machines called enzymes. If it is too cold, the enzymes can't move fast enough to perform the reactions, and if it is too hot, they can become bent out of shape.

Plants also need magnesium. It is used to make chlorophyll, and without it the leaves turn yellow and the process of photosynthesis slows.

Sunlight streams onto the Earth's surface every day, supplying an estimated 175 watts of power for every square metre of our planet. Most of this light is reflected, absorbed or scattered, but some of it is captured by green plants, phytoplankton and cyanobacteria. These organisms then use it to create the building blocks of life, powering almost every living thing.

Cells capable of transforming carbon dioxide and water into sugar and oxygen are known as photosynthetic. They contain pigments that absorb light; when the Sun shines, electrons inside the pigments become excited and break away from their atoms. The cells then shunt these through an 'electron transport chain', storing their energy in molecules called ATP and NADPH. This energy is then used to build sugar molecules. In order to keep the system running, the electrons are replaced by splitting water molecules, creating oxygen in the process.

The most well-known pigment is chlorophyll A, which absorbs red and blue light and reflects green, giving plants their familiar hue.

PHOTOSYNTHESIS IN ACTION

This simple process keeps life on Earth supplied with energy and oxygen

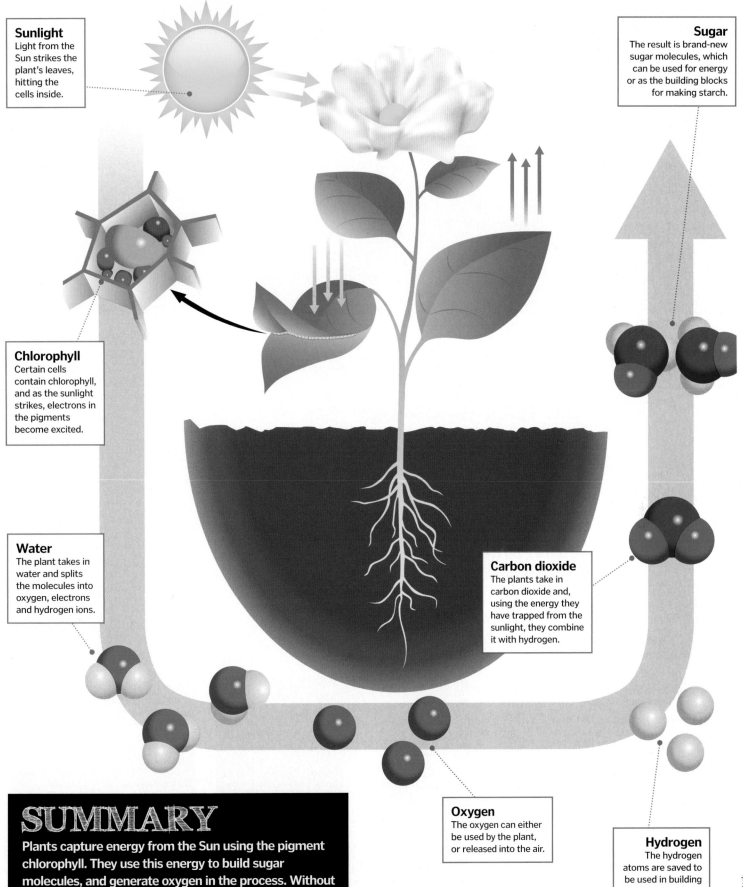

Sunlight
Light from the Sun strikes the plant's leaves, hitting the cells inside.

Sugar
The result is brand-new sugar molecules, which can be used for energy or as the building blocks for making starch.

Chlorophyll
Certain cells contain chlorophyll, and as the sunlight strikes, electrons in the pigments become excited.

Water
The plant takes in water and splits the molecules into oxygen, electrons and hydrogen ions.

Carbon dioxide
The plants take in carbon dioxide and, using the energy they have trapped from the sunlight, they combine it with hydrogen.

Oxygen
The oxygen can either be used by the plant, or released into the air.

Hydrogen
The hydrogen atoms are saved to be used in building sugar molecules in the next stage.

SUMMARY

Plants capture energy from the Sun using the pigment chlorophyll. They use this energy to build sugar molecules, and generate oxygen in the process. Without photosynthesis most life on Earth would not survive.

Planet formation

HOW DO ROCKY PLANETS FORM THROUGHOUT THE UNIVERSE?

As a giant spinning ball of dust circulates around the gravitational pull of a new star, the ball begins to flatten and forms a rotating disc-shaped dust cloud called a protoplanetary disc. This works in a similar way to a ball of dough flattening when it's tossed and spun in the air to make a pizza.

In order to form new rocky planets, little bits of dust need to combine to form clusters. Particles in the disc begin to clump together and as they continue orbiting the star they attract the surrounding material and continue to grow bigger. Under the force of gravity these particles continue to collide into each other to form the beginnings of a planet, known as planetesimals. Over time the star-orbiting planetesimals continue to collide with each other and grow, eventually becoming planetary embryos/protoplanets.

A chance collision between the protoplanets initiates the final stages, and what often remains are multiple fully formed smaller, rocky planets.

Future missions to the gas giants could reveal more about how these worlds form

BACKGROUND

When gases such as hydrogen, helium and other ionised gases combine with space dust, they form an interstellar cloud. Known as a nebula, this giant cloud begins to collapse under its own mass. Gravity then causes this dust and gas to be continuously dragged into the centre of the cloud, making the core very hot and dense. This forms an object called a protostar, which will eventually develop into a new star. Around the protostar, the collapsing cloud forms a rotating disc of material. It is from this 'protoplanetary disc' that new planets are born.

BUILDING GIANTS

Rocky planets aren't the only types of worlds that exist out there in the universe. Often the planets furthest from their parent star are gas giants, which are initially formed from hydrogen and helium.

While the atmosphere of Jupiter and Saturn reflects this, Uranus and Neptune are referred to as the ice giants as they are composed of 'icy' water, ammonia and methane. There are different theories as to exactly how these planets form and what is at their cores. Jupiter is the most controversial of the group, inspiring very different opinions.

In the same way that rocky planets start to form, the predominant theory is that Jupiter also has a rocky core. But other scientists believe that there could be a liquid mass at the centre of this colossal planet. These questions are essential if we are to unravel the mysteries of the universe.

BUILDING PLANETS

How does a rocky world form from dust?

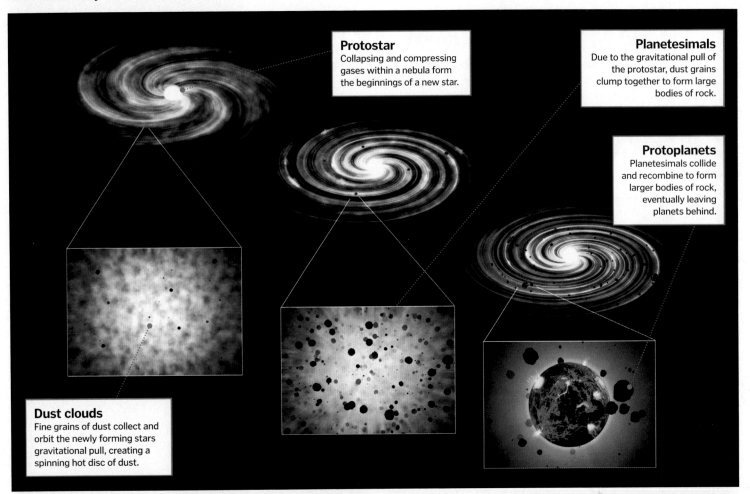

Protostar
Collapsing and compressing gases within a nebula form the beginnings of a new star.

Planetesimals
Due to the gravitational pull of the protostar, dust grains clump together to form large bodies of rock.

Protoplanets
Planetesimals collide and recombine to form larger bodies of rock, eventually leaving planets behind.

Dust clouds
Fine grains of dust collect and orbit the newly forming stars gravitational pull, creating a spinning hot disc of dust.

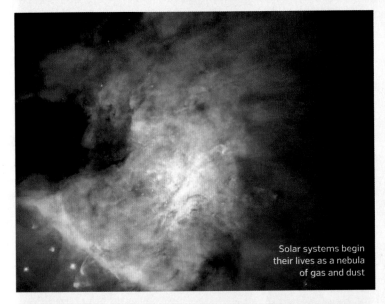

Solar systems begin their lives as a nebula of gas and dust

As a nebula begins to collapse under its own gravity, a protostar forms

SUMMARY

Tiny particles of dust within protoplanetary discs can collide and stick together. These clumps continue to accumulate and collide to form larger rocky bodies, eventually becoming planets.

Make a planetary system

FIND OUT HOW THE SUN AND MOON AFFECT THE EARTH BY CREATING A MINI VERSION AT HOME

You can use this model to replicate eclipses and lunar phases

1 Make the Earth

For this experiment, you'll need modelling clay (in a few different colours), a torch, some pencils.

First, let's make your planet. Roll some modelling clay into a ball around five centimetres in diameter and push a pencil into the centre of it. This will allow you to hold the 'planet' without casting shadows and also make it easier to spin it around when you're simulating the Earth. Place a small blob of different coloured modelling clay onto the ball anywhere you like to represent you.

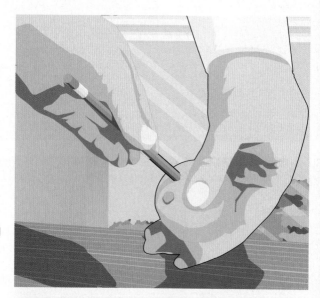

2 Activate the Sun

To create our version of the Sun we'll just use a torch. The experiment works best in a fairly dark room, so turn off the lights and close the curtains. Hold the torch around 25 centimetres from the ball and keep it steady – you can place it on the edge of a surface if it's easier. You'll notice that just over half of your planet is light, with the back of the planet being much darker.

3 Spin and rotate

Start to slowly rotate the pencil under the planet. You'll see the blob of clay that you stuck on slowly moves from the darker side to the lighter side. This simulates how the Sun shines on the Earth as it spins. When the coloured blob of clay is half in light and half in darkness this represents sunrise on Earth. Then, when it is rotated again, it will do the same to represent sunset.

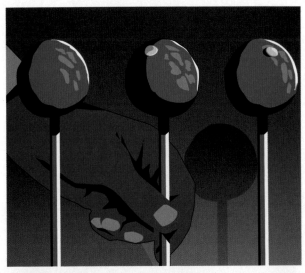

4 Create the Moon

Next, we'll test out the Moon in the same way. Get some more modelling clay and make it into a ball around three centimetres in diameter. Push another pencil into it, then try moving it around the Earth. What happens when the Sun, Moon and Earth all align? When the Moon is either fully in the shadow of the Earth, or casts a shadow on the Earth, it's called an eclipse.

5 Test Moon phases

You can also use your Moon to see how lunar phases work. Hold your Moon model still in front of the torch. Stand with the torch over your shoulder and you'll see a full circle – like a full Moon. Move around so that you are at an angle to the torch and you'll see that the shape appears to change. This is why, when we look at the Moon in the sky, it always looks like a different shape.

SUMMARY

The movements of the Moon around the Earth and the Earth around the Sun are very complex and affect a lot of different things, including seasons, tides and temperatures. This test shows you how sunrises and sunsets work, why the day lasts longer than the night, and why the Moon looks different every night.

Newton's Laws of Motion

THREE SIMPLE LAWS EXPLAIN THE EFFECT OF FORCES ON THE UNIVERSE AROUND US

Sir Isaac Newton developed three fundamental Laws of Motion: the First Law explains what happens if the forces acting on an object are balanced. If an object is not moving, it won't start moving. And, if an object is already moving, it won't stop. This tendency is known as inertia.

Newton's Second Law describes what happens if the forces acting on an object are unbalanced. If more force is applied in one direction, the object will accelerate. The more unbalanced the forces, the faster the object

will accelerate. The more massive the object, the more force that is needed to make it move.

Newton's Third Law explains that for every action there is an equal and opposite reaction. Forces come in pairs; if one object exerts a force on another, the first object will exert an equal force in return. A simple example is the recoil of a gun; as the bullet flies forwards, the gun kicks back.

Newton's laws first appeared in his masterpiece, *Principia*, in 1687, and he developed them to explain why the orbits of the planets are ellipses, not circles.

BACKGROUND

Isaac Newton's famous Laws of Motion explain what happens to objects when forces are applied. A force is a push or a pull, like gravity, friction or magnetism. They can't be seen directly, but their effects can be measured; they can change the speed, shape or direction of movement of an object, and they are responsible for pressure and weight. Newton's three laws describe what happens when forces are balanced or unbalanced, and explain the idea of equal and opposite forces.

SIR ISAAC NEWTON

Sir Isaac Newton was a mathematician, physicist and astronomer, born on Christmas day in 1642 (according to the old Julian calendar). He described the mechanics of the universe with maths and equations in his book, *The Philosophiae Naturalis Principia Mathematica* (commonly known as *Principia*). He explained the concept of gravity, and showed that everything in the universe is governed by the same physical laws. He also worked on colour theory, optics and calculus, and his ideas are still in use over 300 years later.

He was one of the greatest scientists ever to have lived, but his achievements didn't stop there. He built the first practical reflecting telescope and was elected as a Member of Parliament. He even became Master of the Royal Mint, in charge of the production of all of Britain's currency from 1699 until his death in 1727.

NEWTON'S LAWS IN ACTION

The Laws of Motion govern the movement of everything around us

Second Law
As the engines fire, the force of the thrust is greater than the force of gravity. They become unbalanced and the rocket accelerates.

a

Force

First Law
The forces acting on the stationary rocket are balanced. The downward pull of gravity is matched by the upward push of the ground.

Air resistance
A frictional force acts on the rocket as it moves through the air.

Normal force
The Earth exerts an upward force on the rocket.

Reaction from ground

Weight

Gravity
Objects with mass are attracted to one another by the force of gravity.

Applied force
The exhaust from the engine applies a force beneath the rocket.

Thrust

Exhaust

At rest

Acceleration

Third Law
The force that pushes exhaust gas out of the rocket is matched by an equal and opposite force – thrust.

Newton also came up with a law of universal gravitation, reportedly after seeing an apple fall from a tree

A portrait of a 46-year-old Isaac Newton, painted in 1689

SUMMARY

Newton's First Law describes what happens when forces are balanced. His Second Law describes what happens when they are unbalanced. The Third Law explains forces acting in equal and opposite pairs.

© Thinkstock

Archimedes' principle

FIND OUT WHY EVEN HUGE HEAVY BOATS CAN FLOAT ON WATER

The 'eureka' moment reportedly came while Archimedes was taking a bath. When he climbed in, the water level rose and he realised that the volume of water he displaced must be equal to his body's volume. If he was bigger, more water would spill onto the floor. He also noticed that the water must be pressing up against him to support his weight, otherwise he would sink to the bottom. This force is now called buoyancy, and is due to the fact that fluid pressure increases with depth. The buoyant force counteracts the object's weight, pushing up with an equal force. But if the object is heavier than the volume of water it displaces (meaning it is denser than water), it will sink. Using this logic, Archimedes proved that the king's crown was not pure.

BACKGROUND

According to the Roman author Vitruvius, King Hiero II of Syracuse commissioned a goldsmith to make him a crown, but upon receiving it, was not convinced it was pure gold. He asked Archimedes to determine whether he had been ripped off.

Archimedes couldn't melt the crown or damage it, and chemical analysis had not been invented. He had to find alternative means of determining its purity. The experiments that followed were the basis of our understanding of density and buoyancy.

WHY IS IT USEFUL?

It's used to calculate how deep a ship will sink when it's loaded with cargo, which allows engineers to figure out a container ship's maximum load.

Just as Archimedes reportedly verified the king's crown, this principle can still be used to assess the purity of expensive items such as jewellery.

Hydrometers use Archimedes' principle to measure the relative density of specific liquids, by observing how deep an object sinks within them.

Ballast tanks in submarines use this principle to allow the sub to stay at any chosen depth, without floating to the surface or sinking further.

THE THEORY IN ACTION

See how Archimedes' principle works in this simple experiment

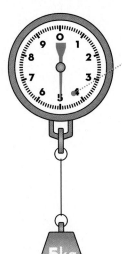

Object's weight
In air and under normal gravity, this object weighs five kilograms.

Reduced weight
As the object displaces two kilograms of water, the object's apparent weight is reduced by this amount, down to only three kilograms.

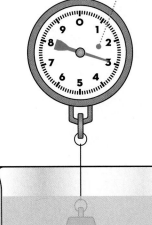

"If an object is heavier than the volume of water it displaces, it will sink"

5kg

2kg

3kg

Buoyant force
Buoyancy counteracts gravity, pushing up with a force equal to the weight of the water that has been displaced.

Volume
The object's volume is equal to the volume of water displaced, a fundamental part of Archimedes' discovery.

Density
This object is denser than the water, so its weight is greater than the weight of the fluid it displaces. This means that it sinks to the bottom.

The buoyant force counteracts an object's weight when it's partially or fully submerged in a fluid

SUMMARY

Fluids exert a buoyant force on objects completely or partially submerged in them, and the size of this force is equal to the weight of the fluid displaced by the object.

Archimedes
287 BCE – 212 BCE

Mathematician, astronomer, engineer and inventor, Archimedes was one of the most brilliant minds in ancient Greece. He was famous for his discoveries about buoyancy and density, his work on pulleys and levers, and his contributions to geometry. It is even reported that he devised a system of mirrors that focused the Sun onto enemy ships to make them combust.

© Thinkstock; WIKI

Make a bubble bottle

CREATE A SIMPLE LAVA LAMP AT HOME USING HOUSEHOLD INGREDIENTS

1 Make it bright

For this experiment you'll need a clear plastic bottle with a lid, water, food colouring, vegetable oil, a fizzy tablet and a torch. You can use a small bottle or a large two-litre bottle, any size works, but large bottles will require more materials!

Fill the bottle around one-third of the way with water, and then add some food colouring; around ten drops should do for smaller bottles. You can use any colour you want, but orange and blue work well.

2 Add some oil

Fill the rest of the bottle almost to the top with vegetable oil. You'll notice the water and oil don't mix; the oil sits on top of the water because it is less dense. They don't mix because water molecules are attracted to each other and the oil molecules are attracted to other oil molecules, so they will not combine and you should be able to see a clear line of separation between the two.

3 Make it bubble

Now drop a fizzy vitamin tablet or an Alka-Seltzer tablet into the bottle to start the fizzing. This will work better if you break the tablet into smaller pieces first. The tablet is made from a mixture of chemicals that react with each other in the presence of water to form carbon dioxide gas. These bubbles are lighter than the liquids, so they rise to the top of the bottle.

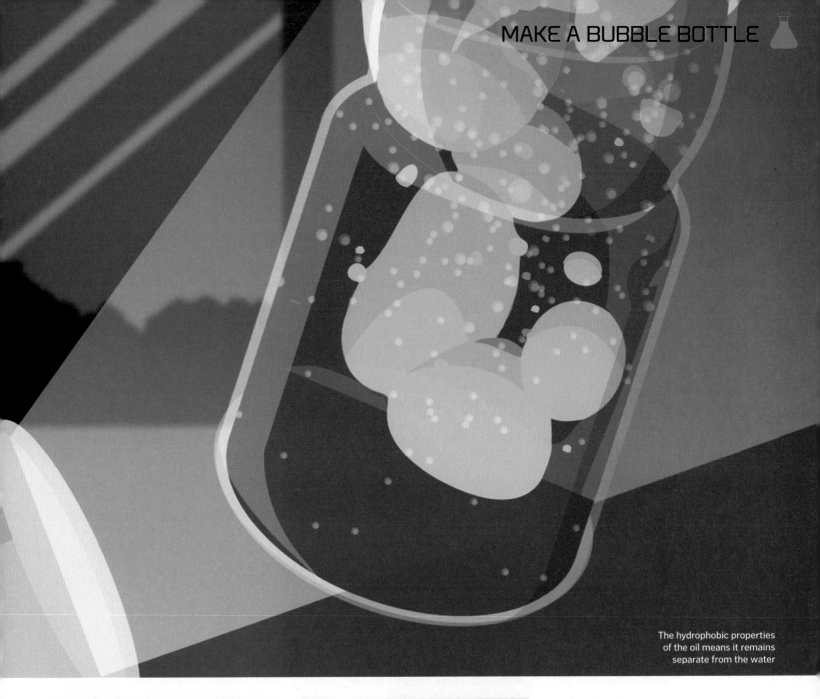

The hydrophobic properties of the oil means it remains separate from the water

4 Light it up

As these bubbles rise they will pull some of the coloured water up with them, making streaks of colour burst through the oil. Put the lid tightly onto the bottle (otherwise it might bubble out of the top) and tip the bottle over a couple of times to make the blobs move even more. If you put a bright flashlight underneath the bottle, it will light up like a real lava lamp!

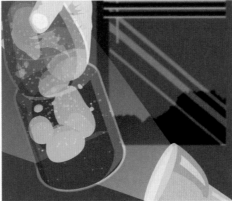

5 Add more stuff

When the bubbles stop appearing, open the lid again and drop in another broken up tablet to start the process all over again. You can also try dropping some raspberries or other small and light fruits into the bottle, as they'll float between the layers of water and oil. See what happens when you add the tablet into the bottle – how does the fruit react to the bubbles?

"If you put a flashlight under the bottle, it will light up like a real lava lamp!"

SUMMARY

The fizzing tablets create carbon dioxide gas in the water, and these bubbles carry some of the coloured water with them as they rise. When they reach the top of the oil, the bubble burst, allowing the gas to escape and the water sinks through the oil. This creates streaks and balls of coloured liquid in the oil, just like a lava lamp!

Internal combustion engines

FOUR SIMPLE STROKES – SUCK, SQUEEZE, BANG, AND BLOW – CHANGED THE WAY WE MOVE FOREVER

The heartbeat of an internal combustion engine is a series of regular controlled explosions.

First comes the 'suck', the intake stroke that draws air and a tiny amount of fuel into the chamber. Then the 'squeeze', the compression stroke, which forces the fuel and air mixture upwards, squashing it against the spark plug. Then there's the 'bang', the combustion stroke; the spark plug fires and the gas explodes. This forces the piston down, driving the crankshaft round. Finally, comes the 'blow', the exhaust stroke, which lets the spent fuel and air mixture out of the engine.

The force of the explosion with every 'bang' is enough to keep the crankshaft turning and the piston pumping through each of the next three stages, cycling up for the exhaust, down to suck new fuel in, up again to squeeze the gas, and then down with the next explosive bang to start the process all over again.

Two 19th-century inventors battle for the title of inventor of the internal combustion engine: Nikolaus Otto (left) and Alphonse Beau de Rochas (right)

BACKGROUND

In 1876, Nikolaus Otto built the first four-stroke internal combustion engine, an invention that revolutionised transportation. The Otto engine controlled, captured and converted energy by compressing air together with fuel and setting it alight. Expanding gas, sliding pistons and turning crankshafts have been powering cars, ships and trains ever since. Modern engineers have added fuel injection, turbo charging and tweaked compression ratios, but combustion engines still use the same simple principles first demonstrated all those years ago.

KEY FIGURES

The four-stroke internal combustion engine undoubtedly changed the world, but it had a rocky start. We often credit Nikolaus Otto with the engine's invention, but it wasn't really his idea.

The key to the success of the four-stroke system was the compression stage, and this was added by someone else. Inventor Alphonse Beau de Rochas realised that squashing the mixture of air and fuel before igniting it would boost the engine's power. He patented the design five years before Otto built his engine, but never got around to making one himself. People manufactured thousands of Otto's engines before anyone realised that it wasn't his design, after all. Despite not having invented the idea, Otto was the one to put the technology into practice. Without him, we might never have seen the engine in action at all.

EASY AS ONE, TWO, THREE, FOUR

Take a look at the inner workings of a four-stroke combustion engine

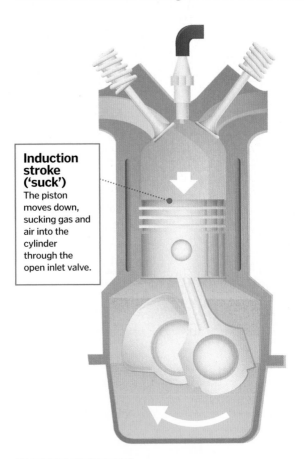

Induction stroke ('suck')
The piston moves down, sucking gas and air into the cylinder through the open inlet valve.

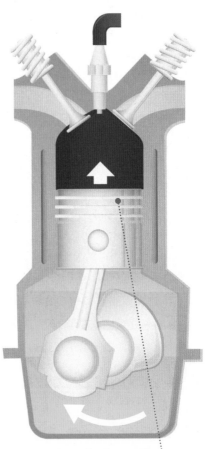

Compression stroke ('squeeze')
The piston pushes up into the cylinder, squeezing the gas mixture against the spark plug.

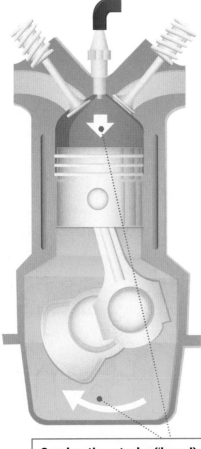

Combustion stroke ('bang')
A spark ignites the mixture and the explosive bang forces the piston down, rotating the crank.

Exhaust stroke ('blow')
The exhaust valve opens as the piston rises, blowing the spent fuel out of the cylinder.

Crankshaft
The crank converts the up-and-down movement of the piston into rotation.

Spark plug
The spark plug delivers the spark that triggers the explosion for combustion.

Inlet and exhaust
Valves at the top of the chamber control fuel in and exhaust out.

The pistons in internal combustion engines turn linear reciprocating motion into rotation

SUMMARY

Internal combustion engines use a four-stroke system to capture the energy released when air and fuel explode. A piston transfers the energy to a crankshaft to power cars, boats and trains.

© Thinkstock

The flu virus is covered in molecules that help it to get inside cells

Bacteria & viruses

WHICH IS WHICH, AND WHY DOES IT EVEN MATTER?

When you've got a sore throat, the cause doesn't always seem important. Some microscopic nasty is waging war with your immune system, it hurts, and you just want to feel better. But whether it's bacteria or a virus on the rampage is actually very important.

Bacteria are some of the smallest living things on the planet, each made from just a single, primitive cell. Their insides are separated from the outside by a fatty membrane and a flexible coat of armour called the cell wall. Their genetic information is carried on loops of DNA, and these contain tiny factories called ribosomes, which use the genetic code to produce the molecules that the bacteria need to grow, divide and survive.

Viruses, on the other hand, are not technically alive. They carry genetic information containing the instructions to build more virus particles, but they don't have the equipment to make molecules themselves. To reproduce, they need to get inside a living cell and hijack its machinery, turning it into a virus factory.

Both bacteria and viruses can cause diseases, but knowing which is the culprit is critical to treating them effectively. Antibiotics can harm bacteria, but have no effect on viruses. Even your own immune system uses different tactics. For bacteria, it unleashes antibodies – projectile weapons that stick invading microbes together, slowing them down and marking them for destruction. For viruses, your immune system can search for any infected cells before initiating a self-destruct sequence to dispose of anything lurking inside. But some viruses are able to endure our defences, and can remain inside us indefinitely.

ANTIBIOTIC RESISTANCE

Antibiotics attack bacteria. They work by interrupting the way that the tiny cells divide, grow and repair. However, if an infection is caused by a virus, antibiotics won't help. Viruses don't work in the same way as bacteria, so antibiotics can't help to fend them off. It might not seem like much of a problem, but every time antibiotics are used, it gives bacteria a chance to learn how to resist them. So every time a patient with a viral infection is given antibiotics, not only will they not get better, but any bacteria lurking in their bodies will have a chance to see the drug and develop defences against it.

"Bacteria are some of the smallest living things, while viruses aren't technically alive"

HEAD TO HEAD

Both are microscopic, but take a closer look and the differences become clear

Cell membrane
The membrane helps to control what goes in and out of the bacterium.

Not alive
Viruses do not possess the tools to make their own molecules, and are missing genes vital for life.

Nucleic acid
Viruses carry genetic information; some in the form of DNA, and others in the form of RNA.

Chromosome
Bacteria carry their genetic code on a chromosome made from DNA.

Plasmid
These small loops of DNA can be transferred between bacterial cells.

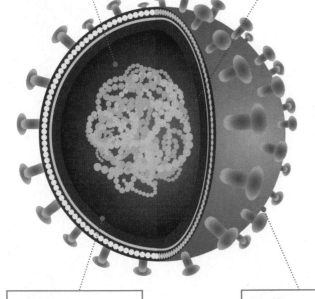

Protein coat
The virus' genetic information is stored inside a protective covering of protein molecules.

Envelope
Some viruses also have an outer envelope, often made from fat and protein.

Cell wall
Bacteria have a protective cell wall, which helps to maintain their structure.

Ribosome
These structures allow bacteria to make the molecules that they need to live.

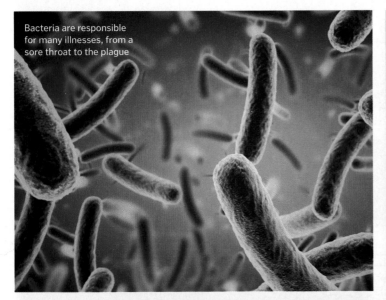

Bacteria are responsible for many illnesses, from a sore throat to the plague

SUMMARY

Bacteria and viruses are different infective agents but both can make us ill. Bacteria are organisms and can survive on their own, whereas viruses aren't considered to be alive and can only reproduce by hijacking organisms' cells.

Viral infections can be mild, such as the common cold, while others can be deadly, like Ebola and smallpox

60 SECOND SCIENCE

Light

A GUIDE TO HOW LIGHT TRAVELS, AND WHY IT MOVES FASTER THAN ANYTHING ELSE

 In 1801, physicist Thomas Young shone a beam of light through a pinhole, and allowed it to hit a piece of card with two slits. If light were carried by particles, it should have passed through the slits, lighting up two distinct spots. Instead, it formed bands, leading him to conclude that light is made up of waves. In 1860, James Clerk Maxwell extended this idea by explaining that light is electromagnetic waves, made up of electric and magnetic fields.

However, in the 1900s, Max Planck and Albert Einstein showed that electromagnetic radiation is divided into packets of energy called quanta, indicating that light is made up of particles, now known as photons.

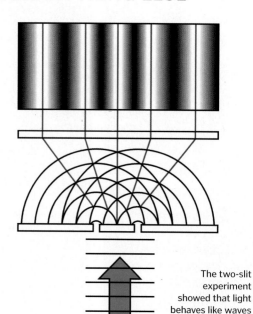

The two-slit experiment showed that light behaves like waves

BACKGROUND

Light is electromagnetic radiation, and the word is mostly used to describe the parts of the spectrum we can see. It travels fast and in straight lines, but exactly how it does this is complicated. Isaac Newton favoured the particle theory, saying that light travelled in packages called 'corpuscles', while 17th century mathematician Christiaan Huygens proposed that light moved via waves, like sound. In fact, light is carried by particles called 'photons', which do travel and behave a bit like waves.

THE SPEED OF LIGHT

The speed of light in a vacuum is 300 million metres per second. This is the speed limit of the universe; nothing can travel faster. But light doesn't always move this fast. In air, water and other materials, light interacts with particles and scatters, slowing it down.

In air, light is only slowed down a little bit, but in water, its speed drops to around 226 million metres per second, and in glass, down to 200 million metres per second. Moving through diamond, it is slower still, at around 150 million metres per second, and researchers at Harvard University managed to slow it down to a measly 17 metres per second by shining it through extremely cold sodium atoms.

SEPARATING THE SPECTRUM

Prisms can be used to reveal the rainbow of colours hidden in white light

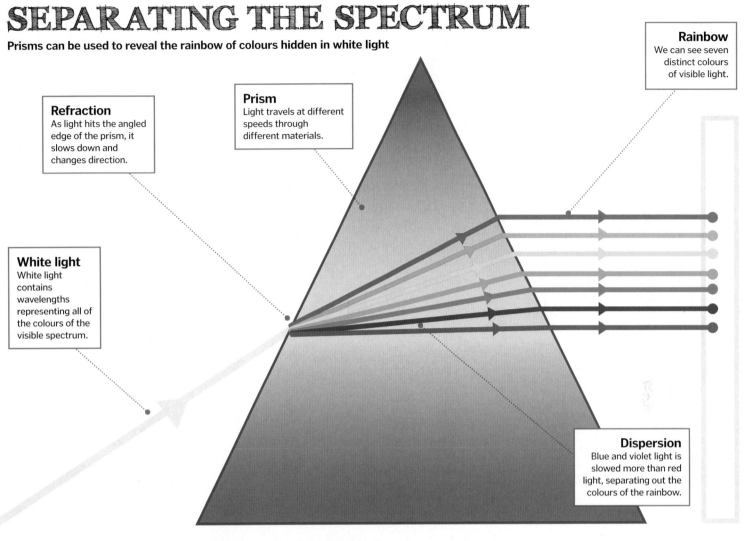

Refraction
As light hits the angled edge of the prism, it slows down and changes direction.

Prism
Light travels at different speeds through different materials.

Rainbow
We can see seven distinct colours of visible light.

White light
White light contains wavelengths representing all of the colours of the visible spectrum.

Dispersion
Blue and violet light is slowed more than red light, separating out the colours of the rainbow.

BENDING THE LIGHT

As light travels from one material to another, its path can bend

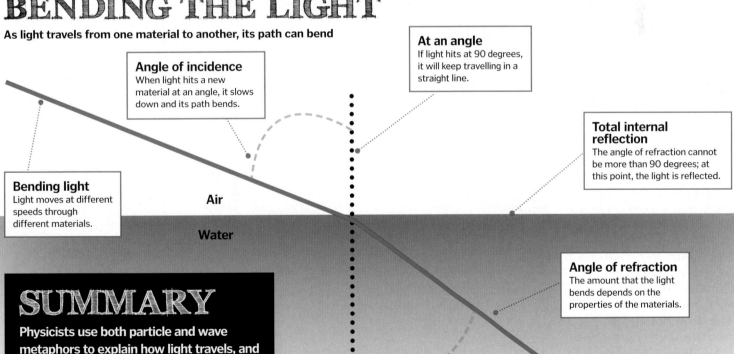

Angle of incidence
When light hits a new material at an angle, it slows down and its path bends.

At an angle
If light hits at 90 degrees, it will keep travelling in a straight line.

Total internal reflection
The angle of refraction cannot be more than 90 degrees; at this point, the light is reflected.

Bending light
Light moves at different speeds through different materials.

Air

Water

Angle of refraction
The amount that the light bends depends on the properties of the materials.

SUMMARY

Physicists use both particle and wave metaphors to explain how light travels, and both ideas are valid. Photons behave like waves, and light can be described as both particles and as waves, or as neither.

Split the colours of light

BUILD YOUR OWN SPECTROSCOPE TO REVEAL LIGHT'S RAINBOW OF COLOURS

1 Make a viewing hole

For this experiment you'll need a large cardboard box, a CD, a pencil, scissors, two razor blades (or card rectangles), a cardboard tube, aluminium foil and sticky tape.

Place the CD on one side of the box just over a centimetre from the edge, and draw around the circular gap in its centre. Centre your cardboard tube over that circle and draw around its edge, then move it slightly to the right and repeat to create an oval. Cut it out using scissors; it must be wide enough for the tube to fit in at an angle.

DON'T DO IT ALONE
If you're under 18, make sure you have an adult with you

2 Position your light slit

Place the box flat on the table so that the oval you've just cut is on the side facing you. Take the CD and place it on the top of the box, so that it is in line with the oval you created in Step 1, and draw around its central gap to show its position. Cut a small rectangle roughly 0.5 centimetres wide and 2.5 centimetres tall, with its base in line with the bottom of the circle you've just drawn.

3 Install your light slit

To make your light slit you should ideally use two razor blades, but if you aren't comfortable handling them use two cardboard rectangles instead. Set the edges of the two blades over the hole you cut in Step 2, leaving a very small gap between them that is the same width at both ends. This will ensure that the light diffracts (splits apart) evenly when it passes through.

White light is made up of all the colours of the rainbow

"The narrow slit will ensure that the light diffracts evenly when it passes through"

4 Tape down your CD

Next, tape your CD to the inside of the box on the opposite edge to your light slit. Its edge must be the same distance from the box's edge as the slit, so measure it with a ruler beforehand. Place the CD with the shiny surface pointing towards the light slit; this will reflect the light to the viewing tube. Cover the edges and any gaps with aluminium foil to make the box light-tight.

5 Complete the assembly

Put the cardboard tube into the first hole you made, angling it towards the CD. Perform a test run before taping it in place by pointing the slit towards a light source and checking that you can see the full spectrum of light through the tube. When you're happy it's right, tape the tube securely to the box. Now you can use your spectroscope to study different light sources!

SUMMARY

White light is made up of wavelengths ranging from red to violet, producing a continuous band of colours when viewed through a spectroscope. The viewing slit diffracts the light into different wavelengths, which reflect off the CD and into the eye. Try comparing a flashlight and a candle!

Vitamins and minerals explained

WHAT ARE MICRONUTRIENTS, AND WHERE CAN YOU FIND THEM?

Vitamins and minerals are essential nutrients. The body needs them to survive, but in much smaller amounts than nutrients like protein, carbohydrates and fats.

The body is made of cells, which are essentially tiny molecular factories. They are surrounded by a fatty membrane, use carbohydrates for fuel, and most of the molecules they produce come in the form of proteins. So the body needs large amounts of fats, carbs and proteins to survive, but it also requires small quantities of micronutrients. Vitamins and minerals are used to produce crucial molecules like enzymes and hormones, which help the body to maintain its balance of fluids, to send short- and long-distance signals, and to strengthen and repair tissues.

Vitamins are organic and made by other living organisms, while minerals are inorganic – most often metals – and are found in the soil. The human body cannot produce them by itself, so we need to take them in through our diets.

There are two main types of vitamin, categorised according to how they dissolve. Fat soluble vitamins can be found in foods like oils, dairy products, eggs, liver and fish, and they are also stored in the fats inside the body. This helps to prevent deficiency, but it means that it is possible to overdose if you eat too much. In contrast, water soluble vitamins cannot be stored by the body. They are found in fruits, vegetables, grains and dairy products, and any excess is rapidly excreted in the urine. This makes it harder to overdose, but easier to become deficient.

Luckily, a healthy, balanced diet is usually enough to ensure that you have the right mixture of vitamins and minerals to keep your body functioning normally.

Vitamin D
Oily fish, red meat, Sun exposure
This vitamin is important in maintaining the right amount of calcium and phosphate, critical for strong bones.

Vitamin B5 aka pantothenic acid
Chicken, beef, potatoes
B5 is used to make Coenzyme A, which breaks down fats and carbs.

Phosphorous
Red meat, poultry, oats
This mineral is found in every cell in the body, and it helps strengthen bones.

Zinc
Meat, shellfish, wheat germ
Zinc is important for making new cells and enzymes.

Vitamin B6 aka pyridoxine
Pork, chicken, fish
B6 is involved in the storage of energy, and in making red blood cells.

Vitamin C aka ascorbic acid
Citrus fruits, strawberries, blackcurrants
This vitamin is involved in the production of collagen, which supports the skin and other tissues.

Vitamin B3 aka niacin
Liver, fish, wheat, sunflower seeds
B3 is involved in breaking carbohydrates down into the simple sugar glucose.

KEY:
Vitamin

Mineral

Vitamin E
Plant oils, nuts, seeds
Vitamin E is an antioxidant that helps to neutralise free radicals. It's important for skin, eyes and the immune system.

Vitamin A
Eggs, cheese, oily fish
Vitamin A is needed for the production of light-sensitive pigments in the eye. It's also involved in immune function and skin health.

Vitamin B12
Meat, fish, milk
B12 is involved in healthy nerves and red blood cells, and helps the body process folic acid.

Folic acid
aka folate
Broccoli, sprouts, liver
Folic acid is involved in the development of the nervous system – crucial during pregnancy.

Chromium
Meat, whole grains, broccoli
Chromium is involved in insulin signalling and maintaining blood sugar levels.

Potassium
Bananas, broccoli, pulses
Potassium works with sodium to pass signals along the nerve cells, helping the heart to function properly.

Molybdenum
Nuts, cereals, peas, beans
Molybdenum helps enzymes involved with making and repairing genetic materials.

Vitamin B2
aka riboflavin
Milk, eggs, fortified cereals
B2 is involved in releasing energy, and it's also an antioxidant that helps to scavenge free radicals.

Vitamin B1
aka thiamin
Fortified cereals, nuts and meats
The first of eight B vitamins involved in breaking down fats and carbs to release energy.

Copper
Nuts, shellfish, offal
This metal is involved in making blood cells.

Selenium
Brazil nuts, fish, meat
Selenium is an ingredient in enzymes that help prevent cell damage.

Vitamin B7
aka biotin
Eggs, nuts, whole grains
This vitamin is essential for the metabolism of fat.

Vitamin K
Green leafy vegetables, cereals
Vitamin K is crucial for blood clotting. It is a component of many of the clotting factors that help to stop bleeding after injury. It also plays a role in bone health.

Manganese
Tea, cereals, peas
Manganese helps with clotting and is important in connective tissue and bone.

Iodine
Seafood, iodised table salt
Iodine is vital for making thyroid hormones, which are responsible for regulating metabolism.

Magnesium
Green leafy vegetables, brown rice, whole grains
This mineral helps the parathyroid glands produce hormones important for bone health.

Iron
Meat, beans, dark green leafy vegetables
Iron is a key component of haemoglobin – the red pigment that carries oxygen around the blood.

Calcium
Dairy products, green leafy vegetables, soya beans
This is the most abundant mineral in the body. It is used to build strong bones, and is involved in the signals that contract and relax muscles.

Sodium
Table salt
Salt contains sodium and chloride, both crucial for fluid balance, and sodium is vital for nerve signalling.

SUMMARY
Vitamins and minerals are vital nutrients that our bodies can't produce on their own, so they must be sourced through our diets. Vitamins are produced by other organisms, while minerals are inorganic.

Hydraulics

THE SCIENCE BEHIND USING LIQUID POWER TO DO HEAVY LIFTING

Gases can be squashed, pushing the molecules closer together to fit into a smaller space, but liquids are hard to compress, as the molecules are close already. Particles bump around as they move, generating pressure. Push on a liquid, and pressure is increased.

In a container with two cylinders and two pistons, connected by a fluid, when you push down on a piston in the first cylinder, it will push a piston up in the second. The pressure is equal to the force applied, divided by the cross-sectional area of the piston.

Put a bigger piston at the other end of the container and the pressure can be used to generate a larger force. You can see why if you rearrange the equation – force is equal to pressure multiplied by cross-sectional area. If the area of the second piston goes up, so does the force generated.

> "A small push can be used to generate a large force elsewhere"

BACKGROUND

Hydraulics is the system of using liquids to produce power. Liquids can't easily be compressed, so pushing on them transmits pressure through them. The pressure is evenly transferred through the liquid, so a small push can be used to create a large force elsewhere. This can be used to move pistons, which in turn can be used to perform work, such as lifting with a crane or braking a car.

PASCAL & PRESSURE

Blaise Pascal was a French mathematician in the 17th century, and responsible for our understanding of pressure and hydraulics. He explained that when you push on fluid in a closed container, the pressure is transmitted equally in all directions. A pressure change at one side of the container is transmitted to all other parts of the container, and to the walls. This is known as Pascal's principle.

His work also included understanding atmospheric pressure. So important were his discoveries that the standard unit for pressure was named the pascal (Pa). Pascal was a polymath, and also worked on the founding principles of probability with Pierre de Fermat.

INSIDE HYDRAULICS

How do hydraulic systems generate so much force?

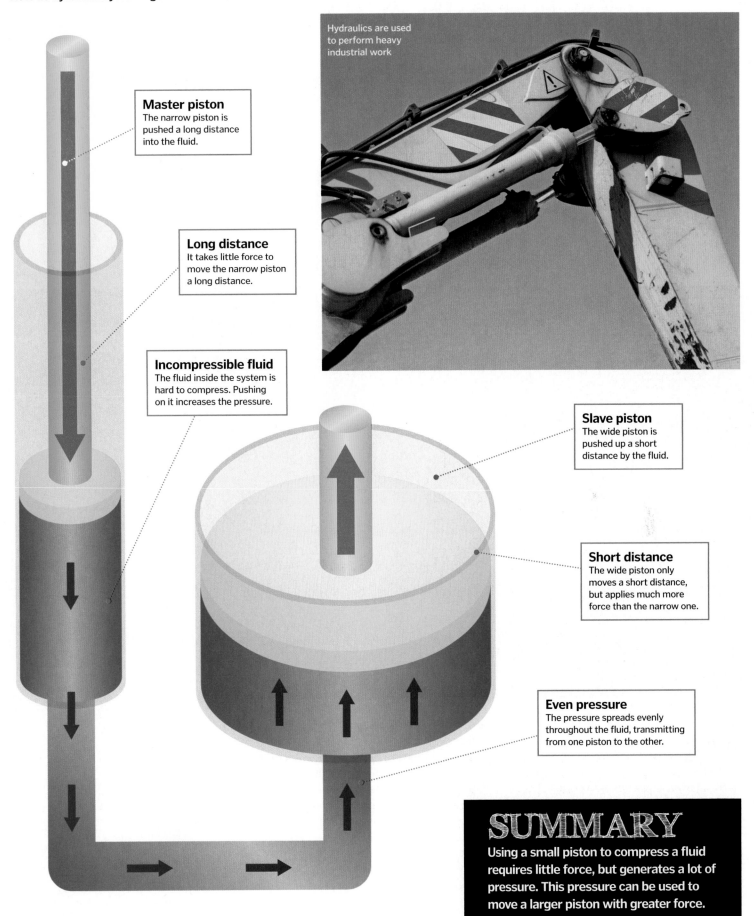

Master piston
The narrow piston is pushed a long distance into the fluid.

Long distance
It takes little force to move the narrow piston a long distance.

Incompressible fluid
The fluid inside the system is hard to compress. Pushing on it increases the pressure.

Hydraulics are used to perform heavy industrial work

Slave piston
The wide piston is pushed up a short distance by the fluid.

Short distance
The wide piston only moves a short distance, but applies much more force than the narrow one.

Even pressure
The pressure spreads evenly throughout the fluid, transmitting from one piston to the other.

SUMMARY

Using a small piston to compress a fluid requires little force, but generates a lot of pressure. This pressure can be used to move a larger piston with greater force.

Journey to the centre of the Earth

WHAT GOES ON INSIDE THIS BIG LUMP OF ROCK WE CALL HOME?

HOW DO WE KNOW WHAT'S INSIDE EARTH?

With no physical samples from the Earth's core, the first step in figuring out what was down there was to work out the planet's mass. This was done by observing the effect the planet's gravity has on objects at the surface. Because the average density of the whole Earth is much higher than the density of material at the surface, it was determined that most of the planet's mass must be at the core. To work out what it is made of, scientists then looked to the universe.

Iron is one of the most common elements in our galaxy, yet it is not very common on Earth's surface, so they worked out that it must have slowly gravitated towards the core over time.

To figure out the size of the core, they then turned to earthquakes. These natural disasters send shock waves through the planet, and so by analysing how they pass from one side to the other, they were able to work out the core's size and consistency.

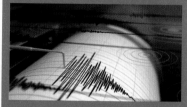

By studying earthquake shock waves, scientists discovered that the Earth's core is both solid and molten

Humans may have circumnavigated the globe, scaled Everest, and even reached the Moon, but we haven't travelled particularly far into our own planet. The deepest we've managed to dig is less than 0.2 per cent of the distance to the Earth's core – so, quite literally, we've barely scratched the surface. Despite this, we still know quite a lot about what's going on inside. For example, we know that, like an onion, Earth consists of several different layers, each with its own unique composition and characteristics.

We also know that, as you go deeper down through they layers of our planet, the pressure and temperature in those layers increases dramatically. This information has made it possible for scientists to recreate the conditions inside the Earth, allowing them to find out what happens to chemistry and biology as you get closer to the core. By crushing samples between pieces of extremely hard material, such as diamond, they can deliver the same pressure experienced towards the centre of our planet, leading to some exciting discoveries.

EARTH'S STRUCTURE

Discover the geology, chemistry and biology of what lies beneath our planet's surface

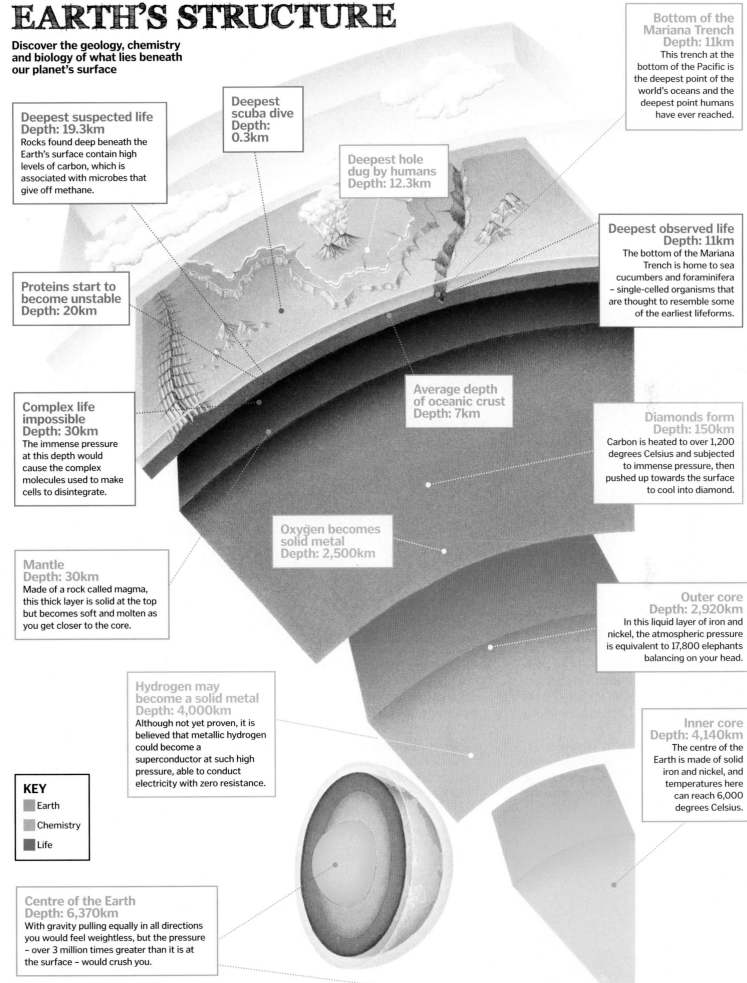

Bottom of the Mariana Trench
Depth: 11km
This trench at the bottom of the Pacific is the deepest point of the world's oceans and the deepest point humans have ever reached.

Deepest suspected life
Depth: 19.3km
Rocks found deep beneath the Earth's surface contain high levels of carbon, which is associated with microbes that give off methane.

Deepest scuba dive
Depth: 0.3km

Deepest hole dug by humans
Depth: 12.3km

Deepest observed life
Depth: 11km
The bottom of the Mariana Trench is home to sea cucumbers and foraminifera – single-celled organisms that are thought to resemble some of the earliest lifeforms.

Proteins start to become unstable
Depth: 20km

Complex life impossible
Depth: 30km
The immense pressure at this depth would cause the complex molecules used to make cells to disintegrate.

Average depth of oceanic crust
Depth: 7km

Diamonds form
Depth: 150km
Carbon is heated to over 1,200 degrees Celsius and subjected to immense pressure, then pushed up towards the surface to cool into diamond.

Oxygen becomes solid metal
Depth: 2,500km

Mantle
Depth: 30km
Made of a rock called magma, this thick layer is solid at the top but becomes soft and molten as you get closer to the core.

Outer core
Depth: 2,920km
In this liquid layer of iron and nickel, the atmospheric pressure is equivalent to 17,800 elephants balancing on your head.

Hydrogen may become a solid metal
Depth: 4,000km
Although not yet proven, it is believed that metallic hydrogen could become a superconductor at such high pressure, able to conduct electricity with zero resistance.

Inner core
Depth: 4,140km
The centre of the Earth is made of solid iron and nickel, and temperatures here can reach 6,000 degrees Celsius.

KEY
- Earth
- Chemistry
- Life

Centre of the Earth
Depth: 6,370km
With gravity pulling equally in all directions you would feel weightless, but the pressure – over 3 million times greater than it is at the surface – would crush you.

The laws of thermodynamics

THE PHYSICS OF HOW ENERGY FLOWS EXPLAINED

Once energy has been converted into its useful form, it can't be recycled

The first law of thermodynamics states that energy is always conserved, so the amount put into a system is the same as the amount that comes out.

However, while the amount of energy remains the same, its usefulness decreases as it changes form. This is the second law of thermodynamics, and it's the reason why there's no such thing as a 100 per cent efficient machine. In other words, energy can't be recycled and some form of energy will need to be added to keep a machine running.

The 'zeroth' law defines the notion of temperature, while the third law states that a substance cannot reach absolute zero (-273.15 degrees Celsius), as its atoms would have no kinetic energy, which is impossible.

BACKGROUND

Energy is what makes everything happen, from getting out of bed to launching a rocket. For these things to occur, there needs to be an energy change – energy must be converted from one form to another. For example, chemical energy from your food is converted into kinetic energy when you move, along with thermal energy, or heat. Thermodynamics is the branch of physics concerned with the relationship between heat and energy. Its four laws govern what happens in every energy change, and are key to understanding the world around us.

THE FOUR LAWS OF THERMODYNAMICS

Zeroth law
If two objects with the same temperature are touching, there is no net flow of energy from one object to the other.

First law
Energy cannot be created or destroyed, it can only be transformed.

Second law
As energy transforms, it becomes less concentrated and therefore less useful.

Third law
It is not possible to get the temperature of a substance down to absolute zero (0 degrees Kelvin or -273.15°C).

"There's no such thing as a machine that's 100% energy efficient"

THE FIRST AND SECOND LAW

See the laws of thermodynamics in action in this simple example

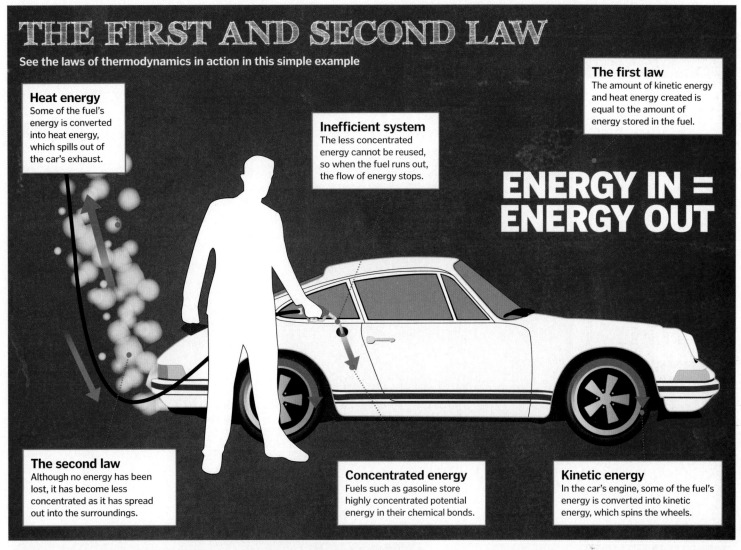

Heat energy
Some of the fuel's energy is converted into heat energy, which spills out of the car's exhaust.

Inefficient system
The less concentrated energy cannot be reused, so when the fuel runs out, the flow of energy stops.

The first law
The amount of kinetic energy and heat energy created is equal to the amount of energy stored in the fuel.

ENERGY IN = ENERGY OUT

The second law
Although no energy has been lost, it has become less concentrated as it has spread out into the surroundings.

Concentrated energy
Fuels such as gasoline store highly concentrated potential energy in their chemical bonds.

Kinetic energy
In the car's engine, some of the fuel's energy is converted into kinetic energy, which spins the wheels.

It's not just mechanical systems – the laws of thermodynamics also apply to living things

SUMMARY

The laws of thermodynamics explain the relationship between all types of energy. These principles are used to understand how all machines work, from human bodies to steam engines.

You are made of stardust

THE ELEMENTS THAT MAKE
UP OUR BODIES WERE FORGED
INSIDE ANCIENT STARS

SUMMARY

All the elements heavier than hydrogen were created either by stellar fusion or supernova explosions. Stars can fuse elements up to the mass of iron, but any elements heavier than that are only produced when massive stars go supernova and release huge amounts of energy. So you really are star stuff!

65% O

Oxygen
Oxygen makes up over half of our body weight. It is one of the key components of water, and is one of the three essential elements needed to make biological molecules like fat and protein.

1.5% Ca

Calcium
Calcium is found in bones and teeth, and also plays an important role in signalling between cells, in muscle and nerve function, and in blood clotting.

18.5% C

Carbon
Carbon can make four bonds to other elements, making it the perfect scaffolding for building large, complex molecules. It is an essential component of fats, proteins, sugars and DNA.

9.5% H

Hydrogen
Hydrogen is the third element found in all biological molecules. There are actually more hydrogen atoms in the body than carbon or oxygen, but they are much lighter.

THE PERIODIC TABLE OF THE ELEMENTS

3.2% N

Nitrogen
Oxygen, carbon and hydrogen make up the core of all biological molecules, but lots of other elements are used in smaller amounts. Nitrogen is found in both DNA and protein.

0.2% S

Sulphur
Sulphur is found in some of the building blocks of protein. It can make strong bonds to other sulphur atoms, helping to fix proteins into their 3D shapes.

0.2% Na

Sodium
Sodium is another electrolyte that carries charge inside the body. Along with potassium and calcium, it is one of the key elements responsible for normal nerve and muscle function.

0.4%

Cl	Mg	Mn	Fe	F	Co
Cu	Zn	Se	Mo	I	Li	Al

And the rest
There are many other trace elements in the human body, including chlorine, magnesium, manganese, iron, fluorine, cobalt, copper, zinc, selenium, molybdenum, iodine, lithium, and aluminium.

1.1% P

Phosphorus
Phosphorus, like calcium, helps to provide strength to bones and teeth. It is also involved in energy use, and is a vital component in DNA, helping to hold the whole structure together.

0.4% K

Potassium
Potassium ions are found dissolved inside cells and in body fluids. They carry an electric charge, and are used by nerve cells and muscle cells in the transmission of electrical impulses.

■ Found in the human body – some others are found only in trace amounts

H																	He
Li	Be											B	C	N	O	F	Ne
Na	Mg											Al	Si	P	S	Cl	Ar
K	Ca	Sc	Ti	V	Cr	Mn	Fe	Co	Ni	Cu	Zn	Ga	Ge	As	Se	Br	Kr
Rb	Sr	Y	Zr	Nb	Mo	Tc	Ru	Rh	Pd	Ag	Cd	In	Sn	Sb	Te	I	Xe
Cs	Ba	Lu	Hf	Ta	W	Re	Os	Ir	Pt	Au	Hg	Tl	Pb	Bi	Po	At	Rn
Fr	Ra	Lr	Rf	Db	Sg	Bh	Hs	Mt	Ds	Rg	Cn	Uut	Fl	Uup	Lv	Uus	Uuo

La	Ce	Pr	Nd	Pm	Sm	Eu	Gd	Tb	Dy	Ho	Er	Tm	Tb
Ac	Th	Pa	U	Np	Pu	Am	Cm	Bk	Cf	Es	Fm	Md	No

*Percentages are by mass

Quantum mechanics

DELVE INTO A WORLD SO SMALL THAT IT BREAKS THE RULES OF CLASSICAL PHYSICS

 Quantum mechanics rests on three key principles. First is quantisation; properties like energy and momentum come in packets, called quanta. This means that, rather than varying continuously, they step up and down by fixed amounts. Second is wave-particle duality; particles are wave-like and waves are particle-like. We need both principles together to explain how matter and light work.

And third, the uncertainty principle; we can't measure everything at once with absolute precision. The surer we are about one of a pair of properties, like position and momentum, the less certain we can be about the value of the other. This makes it impossible to predict what might happen next, only which outcomes are most probable.

The effects of quantum mechanics get larger as things get smaller, and the predictions get weirder, too.

QUANTUM CONCEPTS

Examining the bizarre effects that are experienced at the quantum scale

Superposition
A particle in superposition is in two states at once, so it could represent both a binary 0 and 1. Think of a coin: if it's spinning you can see heads and tails simultaneously.

CLASSICAL PHYSICS   QUANTUM PHYSICS

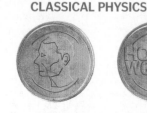

Heads OR tails

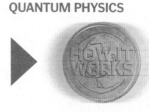

Heads AND tails

Entanglement
Two entangled particles are strangely linked, so the fate of one affects the other. If you observe one particle this will cause its superposition to be lost, and the same will happen to its entangled twin.

QUANTUM PHYSICS

N quantum bits or qubits

HEADS + HEADS
HEADS + TAILS
TAILS + HEADS
TAILS + TAILS

2n possible states

Observation
Observing a particle in superposition causes it to adopt a single state. Any interaction with the environment does the same. The more entangled the particles, the harder it is to maintain superposition.

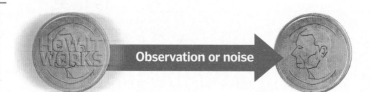

Observation or noise

SCHRÖDINGER'S INFAMOUS CAT

In 1935, physicist Erwin Schrödinger highlighted the absurdity of superposition with this thought experiment featuring an unfortunate feline

SUMMARY
Quantum theory explains the behaviour of small things using packets of energy, particles of light, waves of matter and uncertain predictions about what might happen next.

Steel box
A sealed box conceals the experiment so that no-one can know when the vial breaks.

Cat
If the poison is released, it would kill the cat. Thankfully the experiment was purely hypothetical – Schrödinger never tested it out for real.

Geiger counter
The Geiger counter measures the level of radiation inside the box.

Vial of poison
The vial of poison remains sealed until the hammer strikes. The hammer is released when the Geiger counter detects radiation.

Radioactive substance
There is no way to predict when the radioactive substance in the box will decay.

No radioactive decay

Radioactive decay

Hammer
When the Geiger counter detects radiation, it swings the hammer and strikes the vial.

Poison not released

Poison released

Cat
The cat is alive when it goes in to the box, but will die when the hammer strikes the poison.

Alive or dead?
You can't know if the cat is alive or dead unless you look, so is it both?

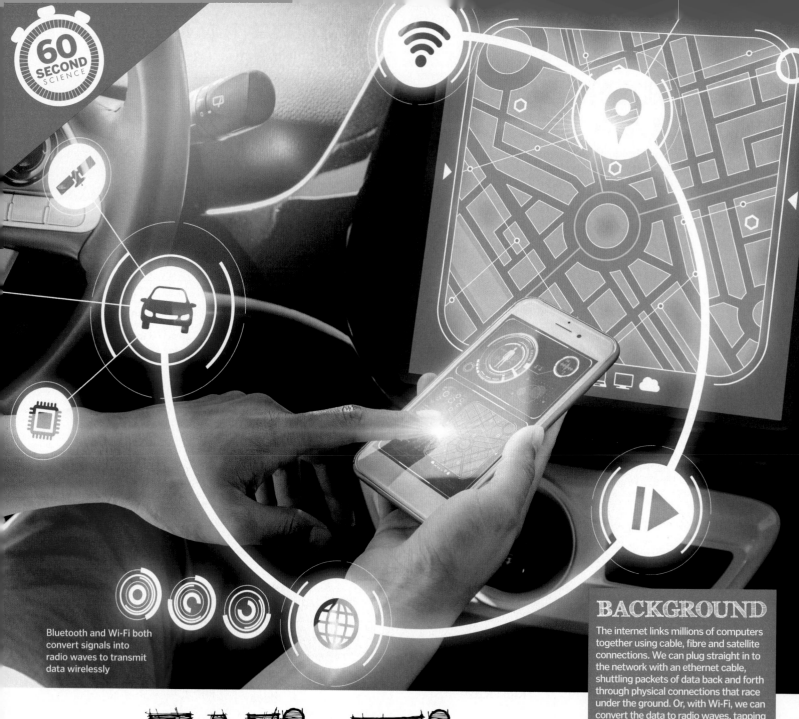

Bluetooth and Wi-Fi both convert signals into radio waves to transmit data wirelessly

Wi-Fi

HOW DO RADIO SIGNALS LINK US UP TO THE PHYSICAL NETWORK THAT POWERS THE INTERNET?

Linking wirelessly to the physical internet network requires a Wi-Fi access point. For example, a broadband modem to talk to the network, and a wireless router to prepare and send the signals. To complete the connection, each device needs a wireless adapter, allowing it to receive and decode the messages being sent.

Computers speak in binary code, so the router and the adapter need to convert the data back and forth into radio signals. They send the signals over one of two bands, 2.4GHz or 5GHz. Each band has dozens of channels, allowing lots of devices to communicate in the same place at once; routers simply switch between channels to find one that's free before establishing a connection. Unlike a wired connection, it's easy for others to listen in on radio signals once they're in the air, so most Wi-Fi systems use encryption to keep data secret.

BACKGROUND

The internet links millions of computers together using cable, fibre and satellite connections. We can plug straight in to the network with an ethernet cable, shuttling packets of data back and forth through physical connections that race under the ground. Or, with Wi-Fi, we can convert the data to radio waves, tapping in without the need for wires. All it takes is a router and a network card to send and receive information through the air.

BLUETOOTH

Like Wi-Fi, Bluetooth uses radio waves to send signals back and forth. But, rather than connect to a worldwide physical network, Bluetooth connections focus on small groups of local machines. Bluetooth has a range of about ten metres or so, allowing temporary exchange of small amounts of data, creating micro networks of up to eight devices.

Bluetooth devices use the same 2.45 GHz band as Wi-Fi and can pick from 79 different channels. Like Wi-Fi, Bluetooth connections use encryption for privacy, and they also use a trick called spread-spectrum frequency hopping. During a Bluetooth connection, pairs of devices switch between channels at random, making it hard for others to listen in.

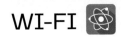

TAPPING IN TO THE INTERNET

What goes on behind the scenes as you scroll through your favourite website?

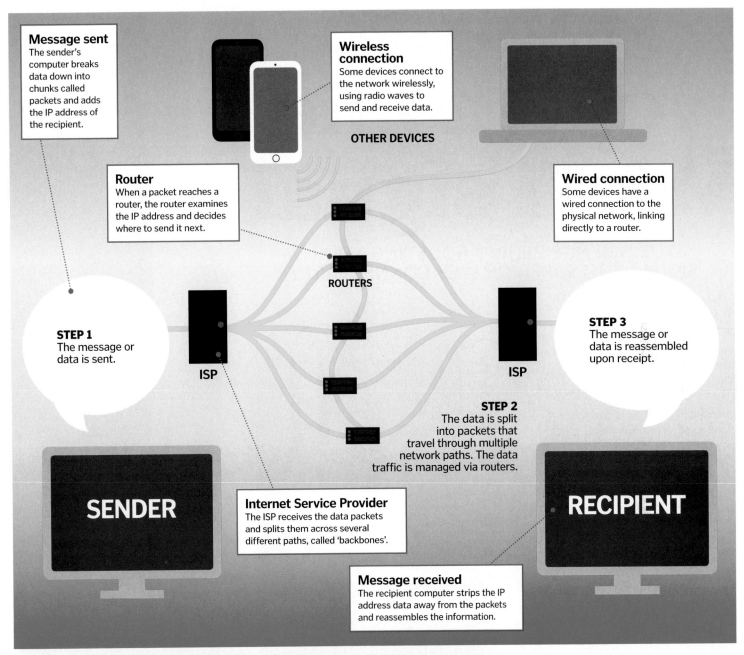

Message sent
The sender's computer breaks data down into chunks called packets and adds the IP address of the recipient.

Wireless connection
Some devices connect to the network wirelessly, using radio waves to send and receive data.

OTHER DEVICES

Wired connection
Some devices have a wired connection to the physical network, linking directly to a router.

Router
When a packet reaches a router, the router examines the IP address and decides where to send it next.

ROUTERS

STEP 1
The message or data is sent.

ISP

STEP 3
The message or data is reassembled upon receipt.

ISP

STEP 2
The data is split into packets that travel through multiple network paths. The data traffic is managed via routers.

SENDER

Internet Service Provider
The ISP receives the data packets and splits them across several different paths, called 'backbones'.

RECIPIENT

Message received
The recipient computer strips the IP address data away from the packets and reassembles the information.

"With Wi-Fi, we can convert data into radio waves, without the need for wires"

SUMMARY
Wi-Fi converts binary code to radio waves to transmit data between the physical network and your computer or phone. Encryption helps to keep wireless connections private.

© Getty

Improve your home Wi-Fi signal

THE SCIENCE BEHIND BOOSTING YOUR SIGNAL FOR SUPERIOR WEB CONNECTIVITY

1 Raise it up

Your Wi-Fi router might not be the most attractive thing in your home, but that doesn't mean you should hide it on the floor behind your TV. Wi-Fi signals travel down and sideways more easily than they travel up, so raise your router by putting it on a table or cabinet to provide better signal throughout your house. It doesn't have to be much, but the higher it is, the better your connection will be.

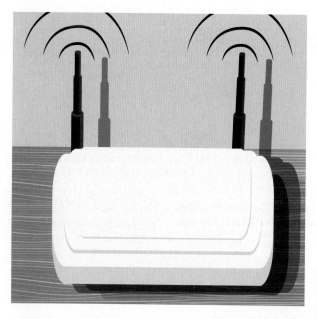

2 The right angle

If your router has an antenna that can be moved and repositioned, it can be tempting to point it towards the devices you use the most. However, this is a bad choice – the signal is actually emitted from the sides of the antenna, so angling it at all will simply result in most of the signal being shot straight into the floor or ceiling. It is best to just keep the antenna pointing vertically.

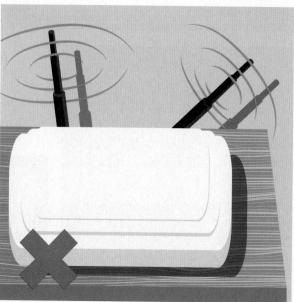

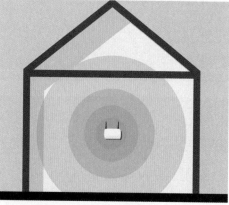

3 Centralise the signal

In many homes, the position of the Wi-Fi router is entirely dependant on where your ports are, but if possible, try to position your router so that it is in the very centre of your house. This will ensure the signal is beamed evenly throughout your home – if you keep your router right up against one wall on the ground floor, upstairs rooms on the other side of the house will suffer.

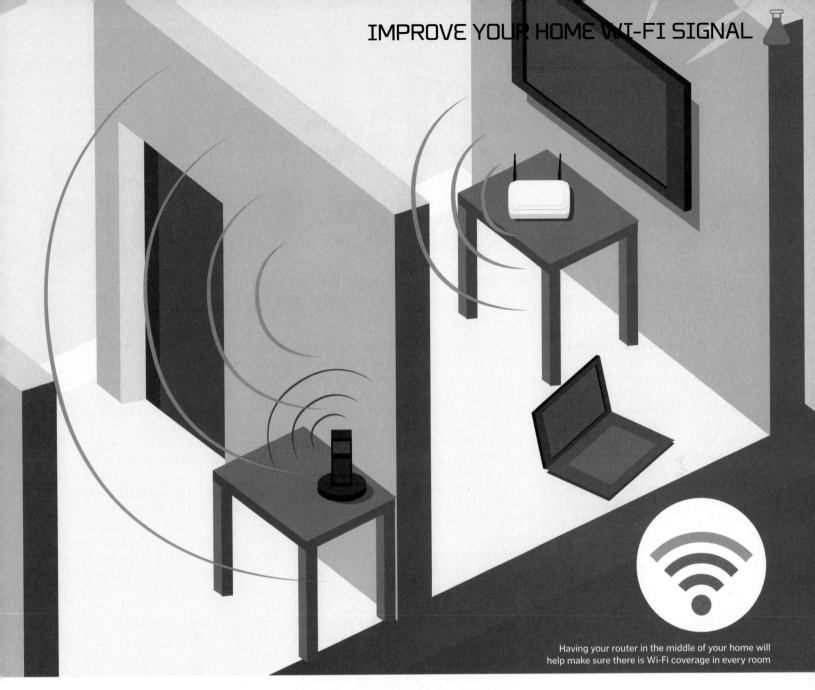

Having your router in the middle of your home will help make sure there is Wi-Fi coverage in every room

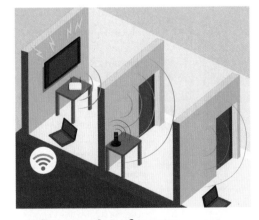

4 Remove interference

We're not talking about knocking down walls here – although thick walls (especially those lined with any form of metal) can disrupt Wi-Fi signals. Instead, try to keep your router away from other electronics and metal objects, and as far as possible from any routers that your neighbours may be using. These things can cause interference that blocks your signal.

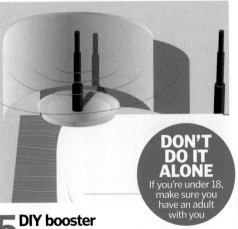

DON'T DO IT ALONE
If you're under 18, make sure you have an adult with you

5 DIY booster

If you can't avoid having your router right by a wall on the far side of your house, try a DIY solution. Carefully cut a large aluminium drinks can so that the thin metal forms a curved sheet. Cut the bottom out of a pie tin and make a hole in the centre. Place the pie tin base over the antenna and position the curved metal to form a 'satellite dish' – this will reflect the signal back into your home.

> "Wi-Fi signals actually travel down and sideways more easily than they travel upwards"

SUMMARY

Your Wi-Fi router converts internet data into radio waves, which it then transmits to your computers and other devices. These waves travel in straight lines and can be weakened if other objects or signals lie in their path – just like when your car radio goes fuzzy when you enter a tunnel.

The periodic table

UNLOCK THE WEALTH OF INFORMATION INSIDE THIS HANDY GUIDE TO ALL THE ELEMENTS

The periodic table makes scientists' jobs easier by providing a visual guide to each chemical element's main properties. An element is a substance made from just one type of atom – carbon, for example. The Big Bang produced a handful of very light elements – mostly hydrogen and helium – which were fused inside stars into many heavier elements, like iron. Add to these another 14 elements produced by radioactive decay and you have our universe's 98 naturally occurring elements.

But the table doesn't end there. By bombarding atomic nuclei with protons or smaller nuclei, scientists have synthesised 20 more elements. Produced inside nuclear reactors or particle colliders, these are the heaviest elements in the table, with atomic numbers 99 to 118. Since they are all radioactive, they decay rapidly – some after a few days or weeks, but many in a few fleeting milliseconds. This leaves scientists very little time to assess the properties of new discoveries. While they await official recognition, these elements are assigned temporary names such as Ununennium (119) and Unbinilium (120).

The periodic table organises all 118 elements in order of increasing atomic number. This long list is then split into rows (called periods) according to how many electron shells each element has. Many of an element's chemical properties are determined by the configuration of electrons sitting in their shells. Elements with just one electron in their outer (valence) shell, for instance, react very easily. Elements in the same column (called a group), meanwhile, have similar electron configurations and therefore share characteristics like reactivity.

A number of other patterns can be found across the entire table. Metallic properties, for example, gradually disappear as you move from the bottom-left corner to the top-right.

PERIODIC TABLE OF ELEMENTS

Non-metals
With a dull finish, non-metals don't conduct heat or electricity well.

Poor metals
These malleable metals have fairly low melting and boiling points.

Metalloids
Despite looking metallic, metalloids are brittle and most act like non-metals.

Halogens
Halogens are just one electron shy of full shells, making them very reactive.

Noble gases
With full outer shells, noble gases rarely react with other elements.

Transition metals
These are hard, with high melting and boiling points.

Alkali metals
With just one electron each, alkali metals are very reactive elements.

Alkaline earth metals
Keen to give up two electrons, these metals bond easily.

Lanthanoids
These soft metallic elements, known as rare earth metals, are very reactive.

Actinoids
Actinoid radioactive elements exist naturally, while others are manmade.

Group	1	2	3	4	5	6	7	8	9	10	11	12	13	14	15	16	17	18
Period																		
1	1 H Hydrogen 1.01																	2 He Helium 4.01
2	3 Li Lithium 6.94	4 Be Beryllium 9.01											5 B Boron 10.81	6 C Carbon 12.01	7 N Nitrogen 14.01	8 O Oxygen 15.99	9 F Fluorine 18.99	10 Ne Neon 20.18
3	11 Na Sodium 22.99	12 Mg Magnesium 24.31											13 Al Aluminium 26.98	14 Si Silicon 28.08	15 P Phosphorus 30.97	16 S Sulfur 32.65	17 Cl Chlorine 35.45	18 Ar Argon 39.95
4	19 K Potassium 39.10	20 Ca Calcium 40.08	21 Sc Scandium 44.96	22 Ti Titanium 47.87	23 V Vanadium 50.94	24 Cr Chromium 51.99	25 Mn Manganese 54.94	26 Fe Iron 55.85	27 Co Cobalt 58.93	28 Ni Nickel 58.69	29 Cu Copper 63.55	30 Zn Zinc 65.38	31 Ga Gallium 69.72	32 Ge Germanium 72.64	33 As Arsenic 74.92	34 Se Selenium 78.96	35 Br Bromine 79.91	36 Kr Krypton 83.79
5	37 Rb Rubidium 85.47	38 Sr Strontium 87.62	39 Y Yttrium 88.91	40 Zr Zirconium 91.22	41 Nb Niob 92.91	42 Mo Molybdenum 95.96	43 Tc Technetium (97.91)	44 Ru Ruthenium 101.07	45 Rh Rhodium 102.91	46 Pd Palladium 106.42	47 Ag Silver 107.87	48 Cd Cadmium 112.41	49 In Indium 114.82	50 Sn Tin 118.71	51 Sb Antimony 121.76	52 Te Tellurium 127.5	53 I Iodine 126.91	54 Xe Xenon 131.29
6	55 Cs Caesium 132.91	56 Ba Barium 137.33	57-71	72 Hf Hafnium 178.49	73 Ta Tantalum 180.95	74 W Tungsten 183.84	75 Re Rhenium 186.21	76 Os Osmium 190.23	77 Ir Iridium 192.22	78 Pt Platinum 195.07	79 Au Gold 196.97	80 Hg Mercury 200.59	81 Tl Thallium 204.38	82 Pb Lead 207.2	83 Bi Bismuth 208.98	84 Po Polonium (208.98)	85 At Astatine (209.98)	86 Rn Radon (222.02)
7	87 Fr Francium (223)	88 Ra Radium (226)	89-103	104 Rf Rutherfordium (261)	105 Db Dubnium (262)	106 Sg Seaborgium (266)	107 Bh Bohrium (264)	108 Hs Hassium (277)	109 Mt Meitnerium (268)	110 Ds Darmstadtium (271)	111 Rg Roentgenium (272)	112 Cn Copernicium (285)	113 Uut Ununtrium (284)	114 Fl Flerovium (289)	115 Uup Ununpentium (288)	116 Lv Livermorium (292)	117 Uus Ununseptium (292)	118 Uuo Ununoctium (294)

Lanthanoids	57 La Lanthanum 138.91	58 Ce Cerium 140.12	59 Pr Praseodymium 140.91	60 Nd Neodymium 144.24	61 Pm Promethium (145)	62 Sm Samarium 150.36	63 Eu Europium 151.96	64 Gd Gadolinium 157.25	65 Tb Terbium 158.92	66 Dy Dysprosium 162.50	67 Ho Holmium 164.93	68 Er Erbium 167.26	69 Tm Thulium 168.93	70 Yb Ytterbium 173.05	71 Lu Lutetium 174.97
Actinoids	89 Ac Actinium (227)	90 Th Thorium 232.04	91 Pa Protactinium 231.04	92 U Uranium 238.02	93 Np Neptunium (237)	94 Pu Plutonium (240)	95 Am Americium (243)	96 Cm Curium (247)	97 Bk Berkelium (247)	98 Cf Californium (251)	99 Es Einsteinium (252)	100 Fm Fermium (257)	101 Md Mendelevium (258)	102 No Nobelium (259)	103 Lr Lawrencium (262)

BUILDING BLOCKS

Take a glance at the key information displayed in each element on the table

Atomic number
The number of protons and electrons in the element.

Chemical symbol
One or two letters used as a short form to represent the element.

12
Mg
Magnesium
24.31

Title
The element's full name for those who don't know their symbols.

Atomic mass
The mass of an atom, which is measured in atomic mass units. This also takes into account the atom's neutrons.

MENDELEEV'S TABLE

Russian chemist Dmitri Mendeleev published one of the earliest versions of the periodic table in 1869, laying the foundations for the table we know today. Ordering over 60 known elements according to their atomic weight, he noticed that elements with similar properties occurred at regular intervals – in other words, periodically. Grouping elements to reflect these trends, three gaps remained. Mendeleev concluded that undiscovered elements must fill these gaps, deducing some of their properties from their position in the table. The discovery of gallium, scandium and germanium soon after confirmed Mendeleev's predictions, and scientists worldwide adopted his table. Over the years, Mendeleev's table has been updated to include previously unknown groups of elements such as the noble gases, and re-ordered by atomic number to create a more accurate arrangement.

GROUPING THE ELEMENTS

The table's 18 groups, displayed in columns, have the most in common due to their shared electron configurations. Trends also exist within groups. For example, as you move from top to bottom, you need more energy to tear an electron away from its atom (ie ionisation energy increases).

Within periods, the table's horizontal rows, similar patterns exist but they are generally weaker. Periods owe their shared characteristics to having the same number of electron shells. Generally, as you move from left to right, elements become more reactive and their size (atomic radius) increases.

Group 18 (noble gases)

2
He
Helium
4,01

10
Ne
Neon
20,18

18
Ar
Argon
39,95

36
Kr
Krypton
83,79

54
Xe
Xenon
131,29

86
Rn
Radon
(222,02)

118
Uuo
Ununoctium
(294)

Helium
Outer shell electrons: **2 (out of 2)**
Protons in nucleus: **2**
How reactive relative to other elements:
Very unreactive

Neon
Outer shell electrons: **8 (out of 8)**
Protons in nucleus: **10**
How reactive relative to other elements:
Very unreactive

Argon
Outer shell electrons: **8 (out of 8)**
Protons in nucleus: **18**
How reactive relative to other elements:
Very unreactive

Krypton
Outer shell electrons: **8 (out of 8)**
Protons in nucleus: **36**
How reactive relative to other elements:
Very unreactive

Xenon
Outer shell electrons: **8 (out of 8)**
Protons in nucleus: **54**
How reactive relative to other elements:
Very unreactive

Radon
Outer shell electrons: **8 (out of 8)**
Protons in nucleus: **86**
How reactive relative to other elements:
Very unreactive

Period 3

11
Na
Sodium
22,99

12
Mg
Magnesium
24,31

13
Al
Aluminium
26,98

14
Si
Silicon
28,08

15
P
Phosphorus
30,97

16
S
Sulfur
32,65

17
Cl
Chlorine
35,45

Sodium
Outer shell electrons: **1**
Protons in nucleus: **11**
How reactive relative to other elements:
Extremely reactive

Silicon
Outer shell electrons: **4**
Protons in nucleus: **14**
How reactive relative to other elements:
Relatively unreactive

Phosphorus
Outer shell electrons: **5**
Protons in nucleus: **15**
How reactive relative to other elements: **Reactive**

Chlorine
Outer shell electrons: **7**
Protons in nucleus: **17**
How reactive relative to other elements:
Highly reactive

Magnesium
Outer shell electrons: **2**
Protons in nucleus: **12**
How reactive relative to other elements:
Highly reactive

Sulphur
Outer shell electrons: **6**
Protons in nucleus: **16**
How reactive relative to other elements:
Reactive

Aluminium
Outer shell electrons: **3**
Protons in nucleus: **13**
How reactive relative to other elements: **Reactive**

Oganesson, Og (formerly Ununoctium, Uuo)
Outer shell electrons: **8 (out of 8)**
Protons in nucleus: **118**
How reactive relative to other elements:
Very unreactive

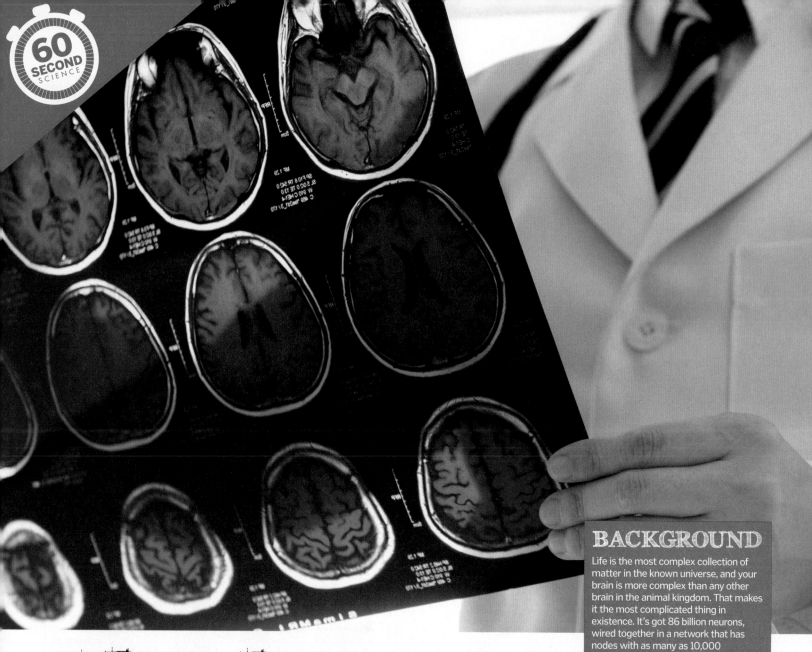

BACKGROUND

Life is the most complex collection of matter in the known universe, and your brain is more complex than any other brain in the animal kingdom. That makes it the most complicated thing in existence. It's got 86 billion neurons, wired together in a network that has nodes with as many as 10,000 connections each. It uses a combination of electrical and chemical signals to control everything from breathing through to consciousness. And, it does all of this in a package weighing less than 1.5 kilograms.

PROBLEMS IN THE BRAIN

There are many ways that an organ as complex as the brain can go wrong. Unpredictable surges of electrical activity can cause seizures in people with epilepsy. Loss of the chemical messenger dopamine can stop the brain sending the messages that control movement, causing Parkinson's disease. And, if cells in the brain start to divide when they shouldn't it can lead to brain tumours. The extra tissue can press on brain cells, causing headaches and problems with vision, movement or personality. Brain cells can also suffer if they don't get a constant supply of oxygen; if a blood clot or a bleed disrupts blood flow, it can cause damage. This is known as a stroke, and the death of brain cells due to lack of oxygen can cause temporary or permanent loss of movement and feeling.

The human brain

IT'S THE MOST COMPLICATED STRUCTURE IN THE KNOWN UNIVERSE, BUT WE'VE MADE IT SIMPLE

It's hard to get to grips with an organ as complex as the brain, but luckily, different regions take charge of different things. At the base of the brain, near the back of the neck, you'll find the medulla oblongata, also known as the brainstem. This is one of the most primitive parts of the brain, and its primary role is to take care of keeping you alive. It manages breathing, heart rate and other vital activities that happen without you even realising. Above and slightly back from the brainstem is the cerebellum. Another ancient part of the brain, this region looks after muscle movement, balance and coordination. The largest part of the brain, the cerebral cortex, is highly folded, allowing vast quantities of brain cells to pack into a small space. It handles the most complex processing tasks, like consciousness, intelligence, language and memory.

INSIDE YOUR MIND

Different parts of the brain take charge of the vital tasks that keep you alive

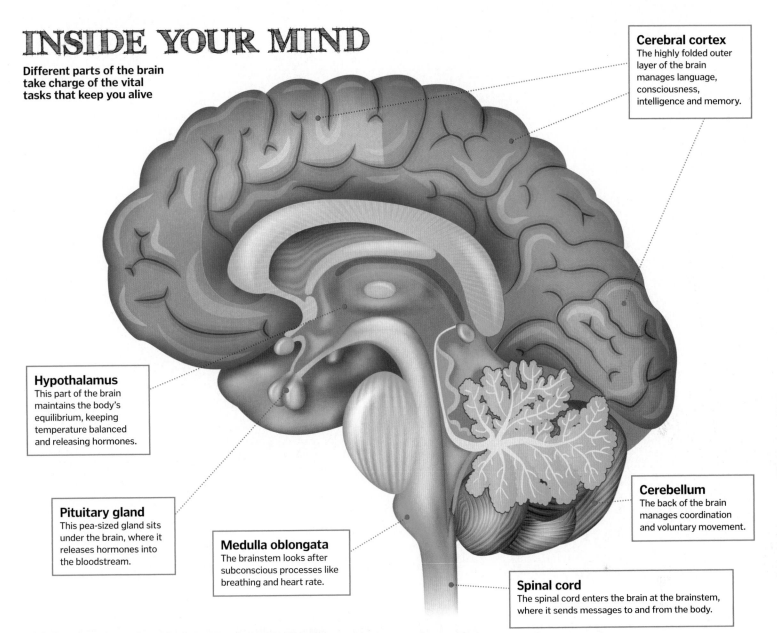

Cerebral cortex
The highly folded outer layer of the brain manages language, consciousness, intelligence and memory.

Hypothalamus
This part of the brain maintains the body's equilibrium, keeping temperature balanced and releasing hormones.

Pituitary gland
This pea-sized gland sits under the brain, where it releases hormones into the bloodstream.

Medulla oblongata
The brainstem looks after subconscious processes like breathing and heart rate.

Cerebellum
The back of the brain manages coordination and voluntary movement.

Spinal cord
The spinal cord enters the brain at the brainstem, where it sends messages to and from the body.

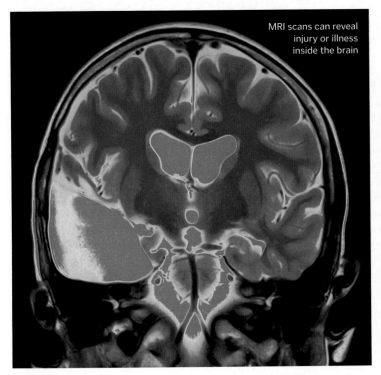

MRI scans can reveal injury or illness inside the brain

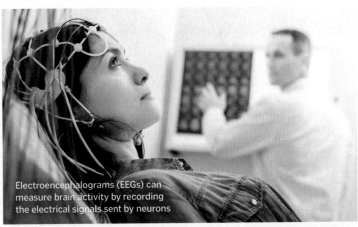

Electroencephalograms (EEGs) can measure brain activity by recording the electrical signals sent by neurons

SUMMARY

The brain has three main parts. The brainstem handles breathing and heart rate. The cerebellum is responsible for movement and coordination. And the cerebral cortex manages thought and perception.

© Thinkstock

091

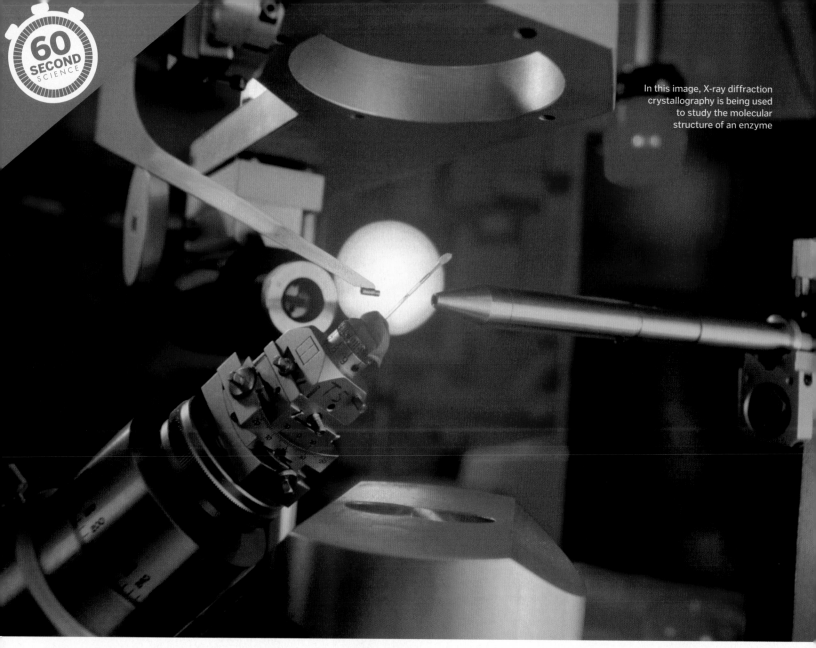

In this image, X-ray diffraction crystallography is being used to study the molecular structure of an enzyme

Crystallography

HOW AND WHY DO WE ANALYSE CRYSTAL STRUCTURES?

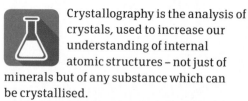

Crystallography is the analysis of crystals, used to increase our understanding of internal atomic structures – not just of minerals but of any substance which can be crystallised.

The practice is centred on the unique geometry of a crystal. First theorised by French physicist Auguste Bravais, all of a substance's angles are measured to find a crystal or lattice system. Co-ordinates are plotted to determine any symmetry, which can then define the atomic structure.

X-ray crystallography was popularised by German physicist Max von Laue in 1912, who showed crystals could be diffracted by this method. Atoms within the crystal diffract the X-rays and the angles of the deflection are measured. Scientists can then map a material's inner structure in great detail.

This innovative technique can be used to determine the structure of organic substances such as proteins and DNA, as well as vitamins, alloys and other composite materials. Crystallography has been an instrumental tool in increasing our understanding atomic structure and bonding.

BACKGROUND

Crystals can be found throughout nature, from salt grains to snowflakes and gemstones. Their atoms are arranged in defined, regular patterns. Crystallography is the examination of a crystalline solid's structure to study the arrangement of its atoms and bonds. By firing X-rays at crystals and recording the diffraction patterns this produces, we can learn more about the material's internal structure.

"Crystallography can determine the structure of proteins, vitamins and DNA"

MAPPING OUT A PROTEIN

How crystallography can help unlock our microbiology

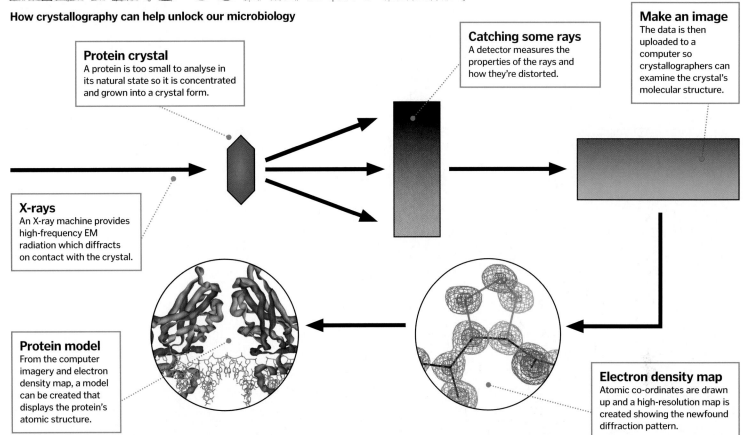

Protein crystal
A protein is too small to analyse in its natural state so it is concentrated and grown into a crystal form.

Catching some rays
A detector measures the properties of the rays and how they're distorted.

Make an image
The data is then uploaded to a computer so crystallographers can examine the crystal's molecular structure.

X-rays
An X-ray machine provides high-frequency EM radiation which diffracts on contact with the crystal.

Protein model
From the computer imagery and electron density map, a model can be created that displays the protein's atomic structure.

Electron density map
Atomic co-ordinates are drawn up and a high-resolution map is created showing the newfound diffraction pattern.

Antimony has a rhombohedral crystal structure

Amethyst crystals are often purple due to iron impurities within their structure

THE ORIGINS OF X-RAY CRYSTALLOGRAPHY

Crystallography is thought to have originated from the work of Max von Laue. The German physicist worked in universities across the country, under the guidance of famous scientists Max Planck and Albert Einstein. He discovered the diffraction of X-rays through the atoms of a crystal in 1912. His results were developed with the help of physicists Paul Knipping and Walter Friedrich and demonstrated the period arrays of atoms in crystals.
Englishman William Bragg and his son Lawrence built on Von Laue's work to create an X-ray spectrometer that analysed the molecular structure of crystals, showing the relative positions of atoms in crystals. Von Laue and the Braggs received the Nobel Prize for Physics in 1914 and 1915, respectively.

Make geode crystals

LEARN HOW TO MAKE YOUR OWN COLOURED CRYSTALS JUST LIKE THOSE INSIDE ROCKS

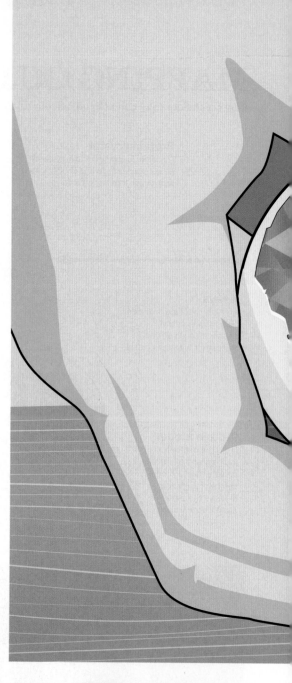

1 Gather your tools

You'll need some eggshells (cracked as close to the narrow end as possible), egg cartons, water, heat-resistant coffee cups, spoons and food colouring. You'll also need to find a collection of soluble solids, which means things that can be dissolved in water. These include salt, sugar and baking soda. You should be able to find some of these at home.

2 Prepare your eggshells

The first thing you need to do is to clean the eggshells with hot water. This will cook the skin on the inside of the shell, known as the egg membrane, which you can peel off using your fingers once you've poured away the water. Make sure all of the skin is removed before continuing to the next step, otherwise mould could grow and ruin your crystals.

3 Make a salty solution

Put your clean eggshells in an egg carton, and then boil some water. Once the water is bubbling nicely, pour some into a cup until it is half full – you'll need one half-full cup of water for every eggshell you've prepared. While the water is still hot, add your soluble solid in spoonfuls to each cup and keep adding and stirring until the solid no longer dissolves.

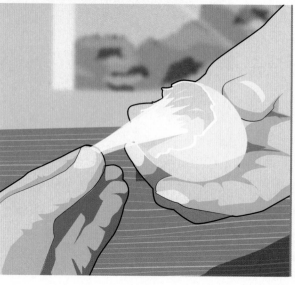

Try the experiment with different food colourings to create a rainbow of crystals

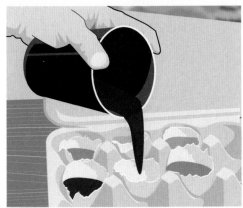

4 Choose your colours

Now it's time to choose what colours you would like your crystals to be. For every cup you've made choose a colour of food colouring and add it to the salty solution, and then we're ready to pour! Add your coloured solution to the eggshell, filling the empty space as much as you can but being careful not to tip the egg or let the solution overflow.

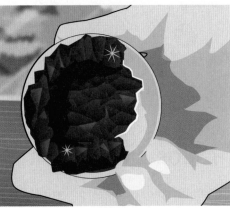

5 Form your crystals

Once you've finished pouring, set your eggshells aside and leave them overnight as the water in the solution slowly evaporates. You will return to find the inside of your shells coated in coloured crystals! These have formed like geodes found in nature, as the solids dissolved in the water have had a chance to slowly come together and form crystal structures.

"The solids dissolved in the water slowly come together and form crystals"

SUMMARY

Geodes look like any other rocks from the outside, but when we break them open we can see that inside they're hollow and lined with crystal structures. By using an eggshell as the exterior round rock and filling it with water saturated with dissolved solids that form crystal structures, we can simulate this amazing natural process.

Fusion versus fission

ATOMS RELEASE VAST AMOUNTS OF ENERGY WHEN THEY COME TOGETHER OR BREAK APART

If atomic nuclei are large, or if they absorb extra neutrons, they can break apart in a process called nuclear fission. As they split, they release more neutrons, which can hit other atoms, making them unstable too. This can trigger a nuclear chain reaction, where the fission of one particle sets off the fission of another and another. Under controlled conditions, we can use water to capture the energy released; the water turns into steam, which spins turbines, powering generators and generate electricity.

Atomic nuclei can also come together to form heavier elements. Nuclei have a positive charge, so to fuse they need to overcome the repulsive forces that keep them apart; this takes intense heat and pressure. In the Sun, hydrogen nuclei squash together to become helium nuclei. The process releases huge amounts of energy, but we haven't yet worked out how to control it to produce power on Earth.

BACKGROUND

Every atom has a nucleus containing positive protons and neutral neutrons. The number of protons determines the type of element, and the number of neutrons the isotope. But, they aren't necessarily fixed. Given the right conditions, atomic nuclei can break apart or come together, splitting into smaller elements or joining to form larger ones. These processes, known as fission and fusion, release huge amounts of energy, powering nuclear reactors, nuclear weapons, and even our own Sun.

DISCOVERING FISSION

Just before World War II broke out, two scientists in Germany were experimenting with neutrons. Otto Hahn and Fritz Strassmann wanted to know what would happen if they fired the particles at high speed into atoms. The answer for most elements was 'not much', but when they tried uranium, something unusual happened. The element broke apart. Even stranger, the mass of the pieces left behind didn't add up to the mass of the uranium they'd started with. As the uranium atoms split apart, some of the mass turned into energy. The collapsing atoms also released more neutrons, which could split even more uranium atoms, releasing even more energy.

News of the discovery reached the United States, where hundreds of scientists worked in secret to turn nuclear fission into one of the deadliest weapons ever seen.

WHAT HAPPENS TO THE ATOMS?

Zoom in on fission and fusion reactions to see how they compare

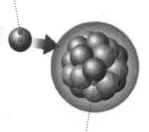

Neutron
A neutron fired into an atom can make the atomic nucleus unstable.

Fission
Atomic nuclei split apart, making smaller atoms and releasing neutrons and energy.

Fusion
Two small nuclei come together to make one heavier element, releasing energy in the process.

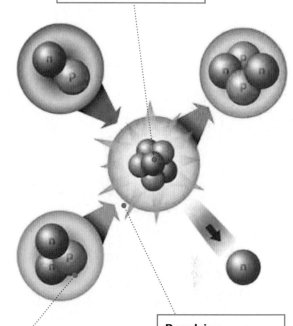

Atomic nucleus
Large atomic nuclei, or atomic nuclei with too many neutrons, can struggle to stay together.

Small nuclei
If there is enough pressure and temperatures are high, small atomic nuclei can squash together.

Repulsion
For fusion to happen, there has to be enough energy to push past the positive charges of the two nuclei.

"Under controlled conditions, we can use water to capture the energy released from fission"

The Little Boy atomic bomb used nuclear fission reactions to create a deadly explosion over Hiroshima

SUMMARY

During nuclear fission, atomic nuclei break apart, forming lighter elements and releasing neutrons. During nuclear fusion, atomic nuclei join together, forming heavier elements. Both processes release energy.

© Getty

Forces

UNDERSTAND THE INVISIBLE POWERS THAT GOVERN EVERYTHING WE DO

Gravity keeps our feet firmly on the floor and tethers the planets into orbits around the stars. Wherever there is matter there is gravity, and without it, the universe as we know it could not exist. Matter would never have condensed to form the first stars after the Big Bang.

The weak force governs nuclear fusion and radioactive decay and is the only force capable of changing the types (or 'flavours') of subatomic particles, which are known as quarks. These particles make up the protons and neutrons that come together to become the nucleus of an atom. There is a hypothetical model of a 'weakless universe', but without the weak force to mediate the fusion reactions that power the stars, it is not known if the model would work.

The electromagnetic force is responsible for the sticking force of friction, and is the reason that solid objects don't move through one another when they collide. It creates the pull of a magnet, and is responsible for the upward force of buoyancy in water. Most importantly, though, the electromagnetic force holds negatively charged electrons in orbital shells around the nucleus of every atom and allows those atoms to come together to form molecules.

The nucleus itself is held together by the nuclear strong force, so if one of these forces were missing, atoms could not exist and neither could the universe that we live in.

BACKGROUND

Isaac Newton was the first to point out that without forces, objects would not move – thereby describing the concept of inertia. From the smallest atoms to the largest stars, everything is governed by four fundamental forces: gravitational force, electromagnetic force, nuclear weak force and nuclear strong force. If any one of these were taken away, with the possible exception of the weak force, the universe as we know it would be unrecognisable.

MEASURING FORCES

Forces cannot be seen, but the effects they have on matter can be used to measure them. When a spring is stretched by a force, it lengthens in proportion to the force applied: if there is twice as much force, the spring will lengthen twice as much. Simply by measuring the length of the spring, the relative magnitude of the force can be determined.

Force is measured in comparison to a standard benchmark; one Newton (N) is equal to the amount of force required to accelerate a mass of one kilogram by one metre per second every second. For example: on Earth, for every kilogram of mass, the force of gravity is 9.8 Newtons (N), so (ignoring the effect of air resistance), if dropped from the roof of a supermarket, a one-kilogram bag of sugar would accelerate toward the ground at a rate of 9.8m/s².

FORCES OF NATURE

Uncovering the four forces that rule the entire universe

Gravitational force
All matter has a gravitational pull but at the atomic level, the force is very weak. The bigger the object, the greater the force, and the effects of gravity can be clearly seen in space.

Cells

Molecular interactions
The electromagnetic force keeps atoms and molecules together.

Molecules

Electromagnetic force
This long-range force is the result of interactions between positively charged protons and negatively charged electrons.

Atomic nucleus
The nucleus of an atom is made up of positively charged protons and neutral neutrons.

Atoms

Strong force
The strong force only acts over an extremely short range, but is able to overcome the repulsion between positively charged protons, holding the nucleus of each atom together.

Elementary particles
The strong force and weak force are transmitted by heavy elementary particles, and can only travel short distances, while the electromagnetic force is transmitted by massless photons and can travel much further.

Quarks

Quark
Protons and neutrons are made up of elementary particles known as quarks. They come in six flavours – up, down, strange, charm, bottom and top.

Quark flavour
The weak force can change one type of quark into another, with a different mass and charge.

Beta emission
A neutron decays into a proton and an anti-neutrino and an electron are ejected from the nucleus of the atom.

Weak force
The weak force is responsible for radioactive decay.

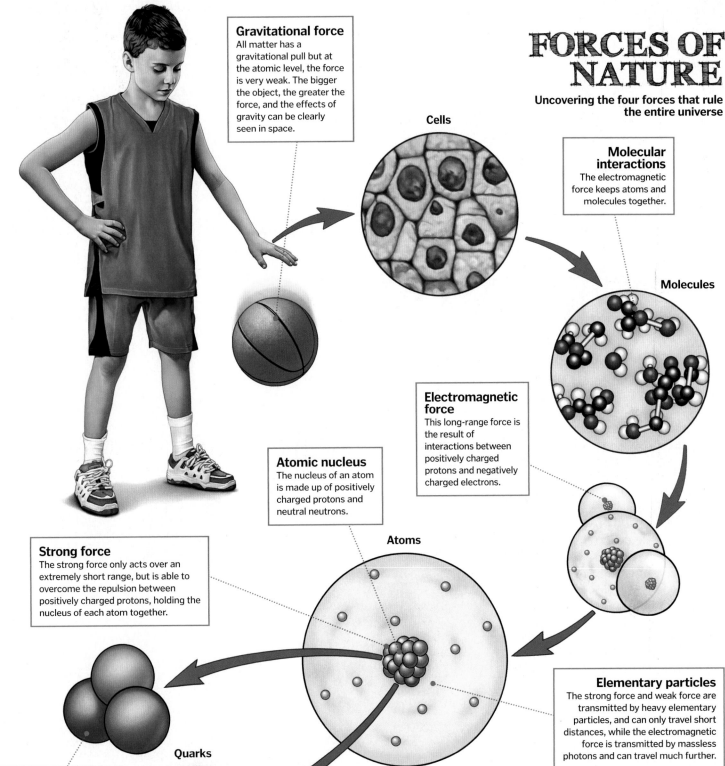

SUMMARY
Four forces govern the universe. The gravitational and electromagnetic forces have infinite range, whereas the strong and weak nuclear forces act at a subatomic level.

Make a teddy bear zip wire

SEND YOUR TEDDY ZOOMING ACROSS THE ROOM WITH THIS SIMPLE ROPESLIDE!

1 Make the wheel

You'll need sandpaper, two old CDs, glue, a plastic pulley, a wooden skewer, two plastic milk bottle caps, some sticky tack, scissors, some string and a teddy.

Using sandpaper, roughen up the central parts of the two CDs, then attach them to a plastic pulley with glue. This pulley needs to have a V-shaped ridge in the middle so that the string of the zip wire runs through it smoothly. Make sure you don't get glue in the V-shaped ridge as you attach it to the CDs! Ensure that the centre of the pulley is lined up with the centre of the two discs.

2 Skewer it!

Now you can place a wooden skewer through the centre of the pulley and CDs that you've put together. Next, take two milk bottle caps and carefully make a hole in the centre of each one. Put the cap on top of some sticky tack when you puncture it so you don't damage your table. Be careful not to make the holes too big, as the caps need to fit tightly onto the skewer. You will also need to make a hole of the same size in the side of each of the bottle tops.

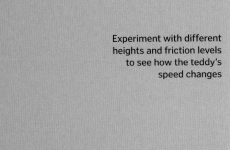
Experiment with different heights and friction levels to see how the teddy's speed changes

3 Put it together

You now need to slide the two bottle tops onto the skewer as well, with one on each side. Make sure that if you hold the lid, the rest of the pulley rotates freely – if it doesn't, try moving the two lids away from the CDs very slightly. Line up the two holes that you previously made in the sides of the bottle tops so that they are both pointing in the same direction.

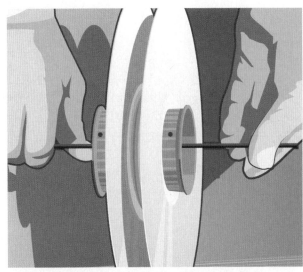

4 Attach your pilot

Now, using a pair of scissors cut off the long parts of the skewer that are sticking out of each side of your pulley, leaving a few centimetres or so on each side. Then thread a piece of string through the hole in the side of the bottle top and tie it to your teddy's arm. Do the same on the other side. Your pilot is ready to go!

5 Test gravity

It's time for launch! Tie a long piece of string across a room so that one end is higher than the other – try tying it to a door handle at one end, feeding it through the pulley and tying it to a chair at the other. Then let your teddy go! The zip wire will speed along as the pulley lets the system roll – if the friction was higher it wouldn't work.

SUMMARY

Gravity causes the teddy to move down the wire, and the rolling pulley reduces the friction to allow it to move. Try pushing the bottle caps closer to the CD – does the pulley system still work? You can also experiment with different slopes or loosen the string slightly so the teddy slows down at the end of the line instead of crashing.

The scale of cells

FIND OUT WHY THE DIMENSIONS OF YOUR BODY'S CELLULAR COMPONENTS ARE TRULY OUT OF THIS WORLD

The average adult human body is around 1.6–1.8 metres in height and packed with some 30 trillion cells. But if you were to take some of your body's individual tissues and cells and place them in a straight line, they would stretch much further. When you consider the dimensions of DNA, these values become truly astronomical.

Most cells in the body contain 23 chromosomes, each of which consists of tightly wound coils of DNA. If you were able to unwind all the DNA in a cell, it would stretch to a cumulative length of about two metres. With an estimated 37.2 trillion cells in the average human body, all this DNA stacked end to end would create a strand 74.7 billion kilometres long, enough to reach from Earth to the Sun and back almost 250 times!

Myelinated neurons

With billions of neurons in the brain alone, it's difficult to estimate the total length of nerve fibres in the human body. A Danish study in 2003 investigated the brain's white matter (consisting of myelinated nerve fibres) and found the average 20-year-old has between 149,000 and 176,000 kilometres worth. This number inevitably rises if the entire brain and the rest of the body are considered.

Blood vessels

Your body contains a vast network of arteries, veins and capillaries to transport blood around the body. The longest vessel is the great saphenous vein, which runs from the thigh to the top of the foot, while the smallest vessels are tiny capillaries. Some capillaries are less than five micrometres (0.005 millimetres) long – less than one-third the width of a human hair.

Red blood cells

It is estimated that there are around 20–30 trillion red blood cells in the average adult, more than all the other cells of the body combined. These cells are among the smallest in the body, approximately six to eight micrometres (0.006-0.008 millimetres). Their tiny size and biconcave disc shape increase their surface-to-volume ratio, enabling them to carry more oxygen.

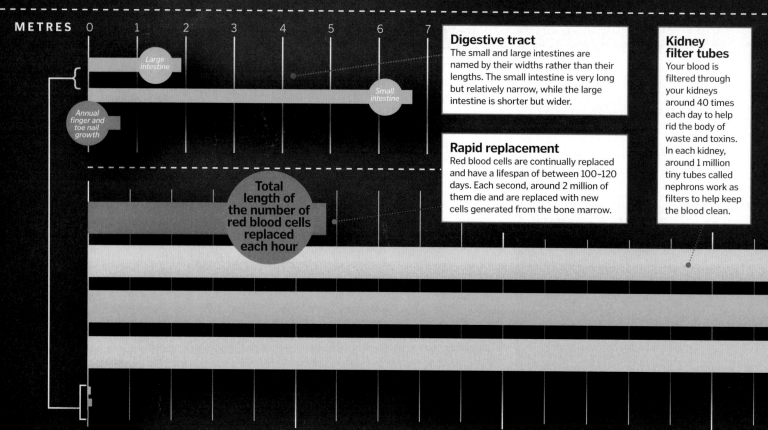

Digestive tract
The small and large intestines are named by their widths rather than their lengths. The small intestine is very long but relatively narrow, while the large intestine is shorter but wider.

Rapid replacement
Red blood cells are continually replaced and have a lifespan of between 100–120 days. Each second, around 2 million of them die and are replaced with new cells generated from the bone marrow.

Kidney filter tubes
Your blood is filtered through your kidneys around 40 times each day to help rid the body of waste and toxins. In each kidney, around 1 million tiny tubes called nephrons work as filters to help keep the blood clean.

(Chart labels) METRES 0 1 2 3 4 5 6 7 — Large intestine — Small intestine — Annual finger and toe nail growth — Total length of the number of red blood cells replaced each hour — KILOMETRES 0 50 100 150

BIGGER THAN YOUR BODY

How your cells, vessels and DNA stack up

DNA
If unravelled, the DNA in the average human body would stretch for a cumulative distance of over 74 billion kilometres.

Up to 176,000km
4.4 times around the world

160,000km
4 times around the world

Up to 240,000km
6 times around the world

Your DNA could stretch to the Sun and back nearly 250 times!

SPACE-SAVING DNA

How is so much DNA packed into the space of a cell nucleus that's only around two to ten microns (0.002-0.01 millimetres) wide?

Each double helix strand is wrapped around proteins called histones to form structures called nucleosomes, which under the microscope have the appearance of beads on a string. These nucleosomes coil up, further compressing the DNA molecule into compact fibres. The fibres are then tightly folded to produce the 250-nanometre-wide fibres that make up chromosomes.

This arrangement is adjustable, so portions of DNA strands can effectively be opened up when the molecule needs to be 'read' during transcription or replication. Since these structural changes are reversible, the DNA reverts to its compact form when these processes are complete.

Superfast signal
Different nerves transmit impulses at different speeds. The fastest are myelinated neurons, which have axons surrounded by a fatty substance that act like insulation around electric cables. These types of nerves are usually responsible for sensory detection, such as sight.

Filter tubes in the kidneys

How far the fastest nerve impulses could travel in an hour

Skin cells

Largest organ
Your skin is your largest organ, covering an area of around

An artist's impression shows what the NAVSTAR satellites look like as they circle the Earth

GPS

EARTH'S SATELLITE SHIELD GIVES US UNPRECEDENTED INFORMATION ABOUT OUR LOCATION

The Global Positioning System (GPS) uses a trick called trilateration to work out where you are. A cage of satellites orbits the Earth at all times, communicating with a series of ground stations and the radio receiver in your phone. No matter where you are, at least four of those satellites are always within your eye line. The ground stations keep track of the satellites using radar, following their exact positions, and the satellites themselves beam radio signals back to the ground. These signals contain information about the time the satellite sent them, and the satellite's position. Using this data, your phone can work out how far away you are, giving you a circle of possible locations around each satellite. It can then narrow down your exact location by working out where the circles cross over, a bit like a Venn diagram.

BACKGROUND

Gone are the days when we had to rely on paper maps and compasses for navigation. Earth is now surrounded by a shield of around 30 satellites that allow us to pinpoint our location to within a range of five meters, if the sky is clear. Combined with digital maps, we can see exactly where we are, plot a route to our destination and track our progress all at the swipe of a thumb.

MILITARY HISTORY

Pioneered by the United States Navy, Department of Defense, and Air Force, modern GPS is military-grade technology. It started life as a series of six submarine-tracking satellites, known as Transit, launched in the 1960s. Following this, 24 Navigation System with Timing and Ranging (NAVSTAR) satellites launched between 1978 and 1993. Each one completes two circles of the Earth every day, and they all move in different orbits, forming a cage around the planet.

The original goal was precision missile targeting, and until 2000, the public didn't have full access to the signals. We received a degraded version of GPS and were only allowed a vague idea of where we were, even though the system was capable of more. But President Clinton eventually lifted the ban and we've been enjoying high-resolution GPS ever since.

BEHIND THE SCENES OF GPS

Have you ever wondered how your phone knows exactly where you're standing?

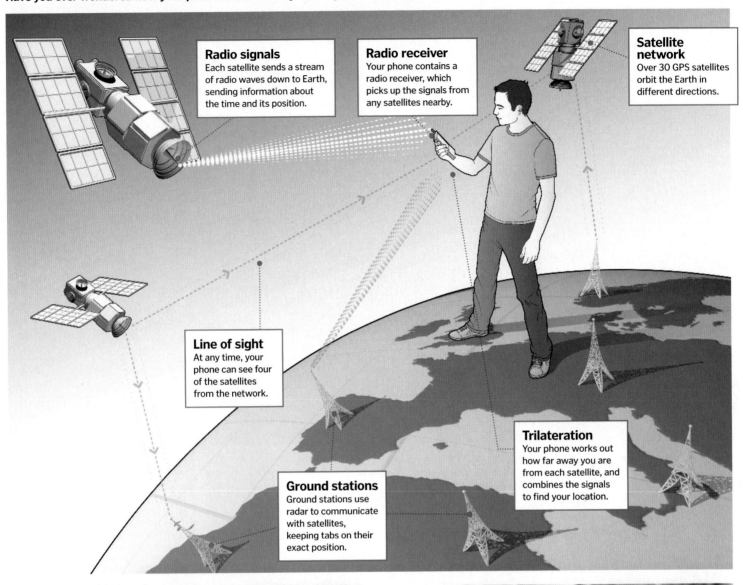

Radio signals
Each satellite sends a stream of radio waves down to Earth, sending information about the time and its position.

Radio receiver
Your phone contains a radio receiver, which picks up the signals from any satellites nearby.

Satellite network
Over 30 GPS satellites orbit the Earth in different directions.

Line of sight
At any time, your phone can see four of the satellites from the network.

Trilateration
Your phone works out how far away you are from each satellite, and combines the signals to find your location.

Ground stations
Ground stations use radar to communicate with satellites, keeping tabs on their exact position.

Ground stations monitor the GPS satellites and help keep track of their locations

SUMMARY

A network of satellites sends radio signals to the ground. Using these signals, your phone can tell you how far away you are from each satellite, and therefore where you're standing on Earth.

GPS can track your location to an accuracy of within a few metres

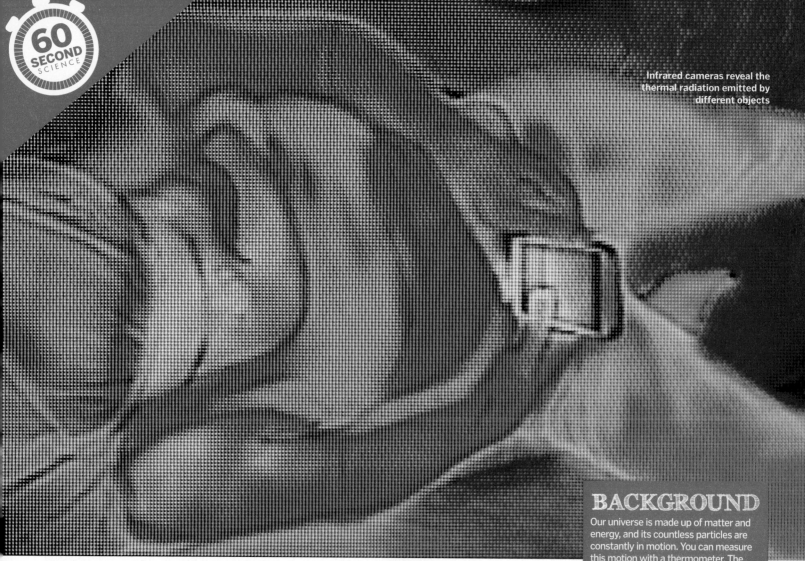
Infrared cameras reveal the thermal radiation emitted by different objects

Heat transfer

GET THE 60-SECOND LOWDOWN ON HOW HEAT GETS FROM A TO B

Conduction is the transfer of heat through solids by the movement of particles. Heat energy is transferred by movement, and if moving particles bash into each other, they pass some of their energy on. Metals are particularly good at conducting heat because they have free electrons that can move around inside, taking heat energy with them.

Convection happens in fluids. When liquids and gasses are heated, the particles inside them move faster. This causes the warm fluid to expand and become less dense, rising above the colder fluid. As the colder fluid is heated, it expands and rises, and as the warm fluid cools, it contracts and falls, creating convection currents.

All objects also emit infrared radiation. The higher the temperature, the more radiation is released. These electromagnetic waves can travel through a vacuum, allowing heat to be transferred even in space.

"Heat is a transfer of energy from one place to another"

BACKGROUND

Our universe is made up of matter and energy, and its countless particles are constantly in motion. You can measure this motion with a thermometer. The temperature tells you the average kinetic (movement) energy – the more the particles are moving, the higher the temperature will be.

Heat is the transfer of this energy from one place to another. If an object feels warm, it's because it is transferring energy to your body. This can happen in three ways: conduction, convection and radiation. This understanding of heat developed in the 1800s and overturned many now obsolete theories that were proposed before it.

ENERGY LAW

Thermodynamics is the science of energy and work. In 1850, scientists Rudolf clausius and William Thomson, (Baron Kelvin, after whom the unit Kelvin is named) stated the first law of thermodynamics, which describes energy conservation. Energy cannot be created or destroyed, but it can travel from one place to another. it can also be converted into other types of energy like chemical, electrical, light and sound.

The first law states that the amount of energy in a system is equal to the heat transfer minus the work done. For example, in a car engine, a spark ignites petrol gas, converting chemical energy into thermal energy and causing the gas to expand inside a closed cylinder. This pushes against a piston and, as the piston moves, it turns the crankshaft. The thermal energy is converted into kinetic energy to move the car.

HEAT TRANSFER IN ACTION

Boiling a pan of water uses all three methods of heat transfer

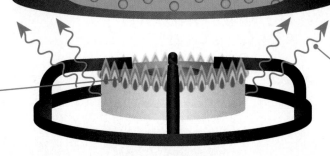

Conduction
The free electrons in the metal pan transfer heat by bumping into molecules and setting them vibrating.

Expansion
The fast-moving water molecules get further apart and the heated water becomes less dense.

Convection
As the water at the bottom of the pan heats up, the molecules move faster.

Convection currents
The cool water drops to the bottom of the pan, before being heated and rising to the top.

Heat source
The combustion reaction in the fire converts chemical energy to thermal energy.

Radiation
Infrared radiation from the flames travels through the air, colliding with the metal of the pan.

A fire transfers heat via convection, conduction and radiation

© Getty

Heat from the Sun is transferred to Earth by radiation

© Getty

SUMMARY

Heat is the transfer of energy by conduction or convection, which both involve particles, or by radiation, a process that involves electromagnetic waves, which can travel through a vacuum.

Make a solar tower

INVESTIGATE AIR DENSITY AND FIND OUT HOW HEAT CAN GENERATE POWER

1 Make your fan

You'll need a rectangle of black card around 30 centimetres long and 25 centimetres wide. You'll also need a piece of paper, some scissors, a long pin, two similarly thick books and a small strip of card. Once you have these items, cut a square of paper ten centimetres wide, then make a cut from each corner towards the middle of the square, around two-thirds of the way to the centre.

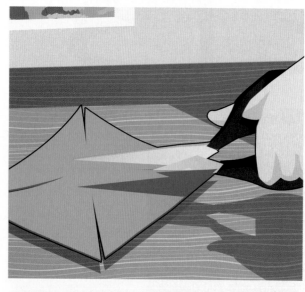

2 Fold it

Now for the slightly fiddly part. Take one corner of the paper at a time and fold it in so that it touches the centre point of the square. This will create a kind of 'pocket' in the paper. Do the same with the other three corners, ensuring that these pockets all face the same direction, like the blades of a fan. Glue the folded paper in place at the centre of the square.

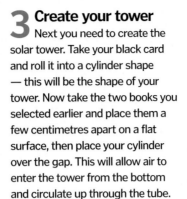

3 Create your tower

Next you need to create the solar tower. Take your black card and roll it into a cylinder shape — this will be the shape of your tower. Now take the two books you selected earlier and place them a few centimetres apart on a flat surface, then place your cylinder over the gap. This will allow air to enter the tower from the bottom and circulate up through the tube.

4 Add your fan

Take a small strip of card and bend it slightly to create a C-shaped piece. Stick this to the top of your tower on the inside to create a loop that looks a little bit like a handle for your cylinder. Then push the pin through the middle of one of your folded fans and wiggle it around a bit so the hole is just big enough for the fan to spin without too much resistance. Pin the whole thing about half way through the C-shaped strip of card so that it sits just above the tower's opening.

5 See your solar tower in action

Now place your tower near a sunny window to see what happens. Black items absorb heat, so by using black card you have created a tower that warms up the air inside it. What happens at it gets hotter? You should see that the fan on top starts to move as air is pushed up through the tube and cooler air is pulled in from the bottom.

On a sunny day your fan should spin as the air in the tower is heated

SUMMARY

When the heat absorbed by the black tube is passed onto the air inside the tube, the air becomes less dense and starts to rise. As it moves up through the tower and out of the top it makes the fan spin.

Digestion

UNRAVELLING ALL NINE METRES OF YOUR DIGESTIVE SYSTEM

 Digestion begins in the mouth. As you chew your food, saliva is released, lubricating the food and kick-starting the break down of carbohydrates with the enzyme amylase. When it's time to swallow, your tongue comes upward and the food is pushed to the back of your throat. As you swallow, you pass control of digestion over to your automatic motor functions. The mouthful is pushed all the way down the oesophagus to the stomach.

The cells lining the stomach walls pump out hydrochloric acid and protein-digesting enzymes. The presence of food triggers stretch receptors in the stomach lining, which in turn trigger a series of rhythmic contractions. These churn the stomach contents, mixing in the acid and enzymes to grind down the food. This ensures that by the time it reaches the small intestine, your food is a runny, slightly lumpy paste, and is ready for the next stage.

The small intestine is the site of chemical digestion. Here, the pancreas adds digestive enzymes, and the liver adds a generous squirt of alkaline bile, delivered via the gall bladder. This bile not only neutralises the burning stomach acid, it also acts a little like washing-up liquid on dirty dinner dishes, helping to separate the food particles and forcing fats to disperse into tiny bubbles. As the nutrients are released, they are then absorbed over the walls of the intestine and into the bloodstream.

By the time food gets to the large intestine most of the useful material has been absorbed into the bloodstream. In the colon, bacteria help to break down even more of the undigested food. The large intestine absorbs most of the remaining water, leaving behind a combination of undigested material, dead cells and bacteria. When the waste reaches the end of the colon it goes to the rectum for storage until there is a convenient time to get rid of it.

BACKGROUND

Digestion is the process of breaking down food and extracting nutrients from it. Your body's digestive tract is a long, muscular tube that runs the entire length of your torso. It is separated into five distinct sections, each with its own specialised function: the mouth, oesophagus, stomach, small intestine and large intestine.

ONE-WAY SYSTEM

As food makes its way through your digestive system, there are several features that stop it coming back up or going the wrong way.

As you swallow, a flap of skin called the epiglottis folds down to cover the voice box and the entrance to the lungs before the food is pushed down.

When the food reaches your stomach, it passes through a ring of muscle known as the cardiac sphincter, which prevents it from coming back out the way it came in.

To ensure that everything keeps moving through the system, every five to ten minutes a wave of muscle contractions begins at the stomach and travels all the way down the intestines. Known as the migrating motor complex (MMC), this wave squeezes the digestive system like a tube of toothpaste, urging its contents further toward the colon.

JOURNEY OF YOUR FOOD

It can take up to 48 hours for a meal to travel through your body

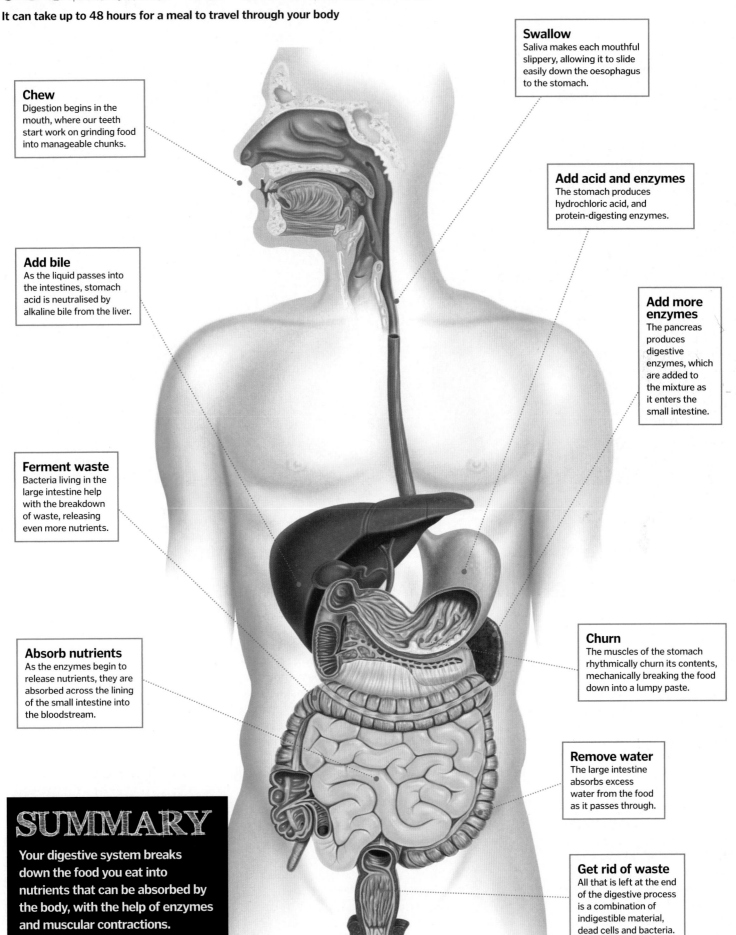

Chew
Digestion begins in the mouth, where our teeth start work on grinding food into manageable chunks.

Swallow
Saliva makes each mouthful slippery, allowing it to slide easily down the oesophagus to the stomach.

Add acid and enzymes
The stomach produces hydrochloric acid, and protein-digesting enzymes.

Add bile
As the liquid passes into the intestines, stomach acid is neutralised by alkaline bile from the liver.

Add more enzymes
The pancreas produces digestive enzymes, which are added to the mixture as it enters the small intestine.

Ferment waste
Bacteria living in the large intestine help with the breakdown of waste, releasing even more nutrients.

Absorb nutrients
As the enzymes begin to release nutrients, they are absorbed across the lining of the small intestine into the bloodstream.

Churn
The muscles of the stomach rhythmically churn its contents, mechanically breaking the food down into a lumpy paste.

Remove water
The large intestine absorbs excess water from the food as it passes through.

Get rid of waste
All that is left at the end of the digestive process is a combination of indigestible material, dead cells and bacteria.

SUMMARY
Your digestive system breaks down the food you eat into nutrients that can be absorbed by the body, with the help of enzymes and muscular contractions.

© Getty

111

60 SECOND SCIENCE

The copper coils at the heart of a electromagnet. The more coils, the stronger the force produced

© Ulfbastel

Electromagnetism

HOW ELECTRICITY AND MAGNETISM COMBINE TO PRODUCE ONE OF THE MOST CRUCIAL FORCES ON THE PLANET

Electric and magnetic forces are detected in regions known as electric and magnetic fields. These travel together through space as electromagnetic radiation, with the fields sustaining each other. Examples of electromagnetic waves include visible light, X-rays and radio waves. In addition, all electromagnetic waves travel at the speed of light – this is how your television is able to receive images live – while force is transferred by carrier particles known as photons.

Crucially, both electric and magnetic fields can produce each other merely by changing charge and position. This principle is today used in electric motors worldwide, as well as electrical generators, where a rotating magnetic field produces an electric current.

"Both electric and magnetic fields can produce each other merely by changing charge and position"

BACKGROUND

Electricity and magnetism were initially considered separate forces. However in 1873 physicist James Clerk Maxwell showed that despite the two behaving quite differently alone – electric forces rely on electric charges in motion or at rest, while magnetic forces are produced by and act on only moving charges – together they work in unison as an electromagnetic force.

THE ELECTROMAGNETIC FORCE

Electromagnetism is one of the four fundamental forces of nature – the other three being gravity, the weak force (radioactive decay) and the strong force (which binds protons and neutrons together to form the nucleus of an atom) – see page 98 for more about those.

Of the four, the electromagnetic force is responsible for the majority of physical and chemical properties of atoms and molecules, which are pervasive in everyday life. These include those exhibited when you push or pull any physical object, such as a chair or shopping trolley, or when you use an electrical appliance. For example, radios receive their audio information via electromagnetic waves carried through space, while laser printers attract particles of ink to the paper via electrostatic force.

HOW A SCRAPYARD ELECTROMAGNET WORKS

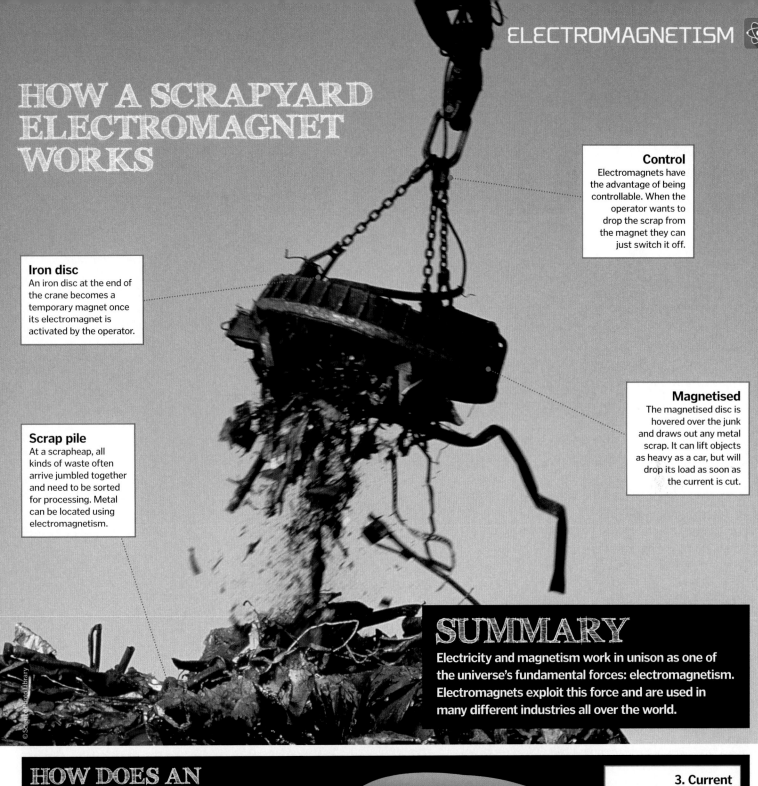

Control
Electromagnets have the advantage of being controllable. When the operator wants to drop the scrap from the magnet they can just switch it off.

Iron disc
An iron disc at the end of the crane becomes a temporary magnet once its electromagnet is activated by the operator.

Scrap pile
At a scrapheap, all kinds of waste often arrive jumbled together and need to be sorted for processing. Metal can be located using electromagnetism.

Magnetised
The magnetised disc is hovered over the junk and draws out any metal scrap. It can lift objects as heavy as a car, but will drop its load as soon as the current is cut.

SUMMARY
Electricity and magnetism work in unison as one of the universe's fundamental forces: electromagnetism. Electromagnets exploit this force and are used in many different industries all over the world.

HOW DOES AN ELECTROMAGNET WORK?

When a conducting material, such as a current-carrying wire, moves through a magnetic field its electrons experience a force. Positive charges move to one end of the material, and negative to the other. If it is connected in a circuit, this will cause a current to flow through the material, like a battery (which has a positive and a negative end). This is called electromagnetic induction.

If the conducting material and magnet are moving relative to each other – such as one rotating around the other – then an electromotive force is produced. An electromotive force is what generates electric power in a power station, for example.

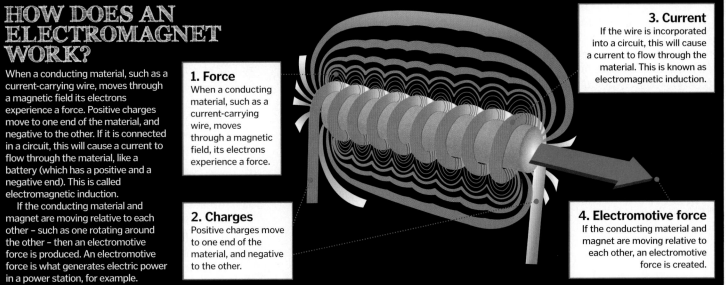

1. Force
When a conducting material, such as a current-carrying wire, moves through a magnetic field, its electrons experience a force.

2. Charges
Positive charges move to one end of the material, and negative to the other.

3. Current
If the wire is incorporated into a circuit, this will cause a current to flow through the material. This is known as electromagnetic induction.

4. Electromotive force
If the conducting material and magnet are moving relative to each other, an electromotive force is created.

Build an electric motor

FIND OUT HOW EVERYDAY ITEMS CAN TURN ELECTRIC ENERGY INTO MOTION

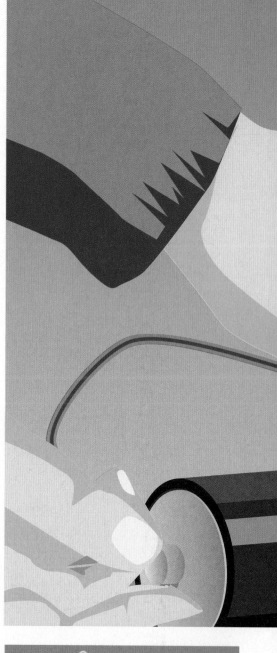

1 Create your electromagnet coil

You will need a D-cell battery, at least 0.9 metres of insulated wire, paper clips, a plastic cup, pliers, rubber bands, two disc magnets, and a pair of crocodile clip wires.

Make a coil with your long piece of insulated wire. Wrap it tightly around the battery at least seven times. Do this evenly, as an uneven distribution of weight will mean the coil is unable to rotate properly. Tie off the coil by wrapping the ends around the middle to hold it together, as pictured, and then strip the insulation from both ends.

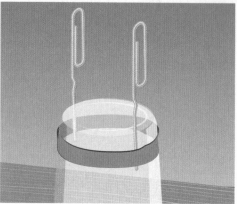

2 Prepare your paper clips

In this experiment the paper clips serve several purposes. They need to be able to support the coil and enable it to rotate freely, as well as conduct electricity to the coil. Using your fingers, or pliers if you find it easier, straighten out the larger loops in two paper clips. The remaining loop in each paper clip will support the ends of the coil once the motor is assembled.

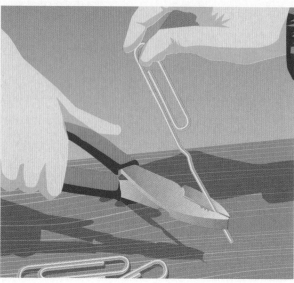

3 Attach your paper clips

Take the plastic cup and place it upside down on a flat surface. You may prefer to cut this so that it has less height, but this is difficult to do evenly so we recommend leaving the cup whole instead. To attach the paper clips, place two rubber bands around the plastic cup and slot the ends of the paper clips in between them. Make sure that the paper clips are secure and level.

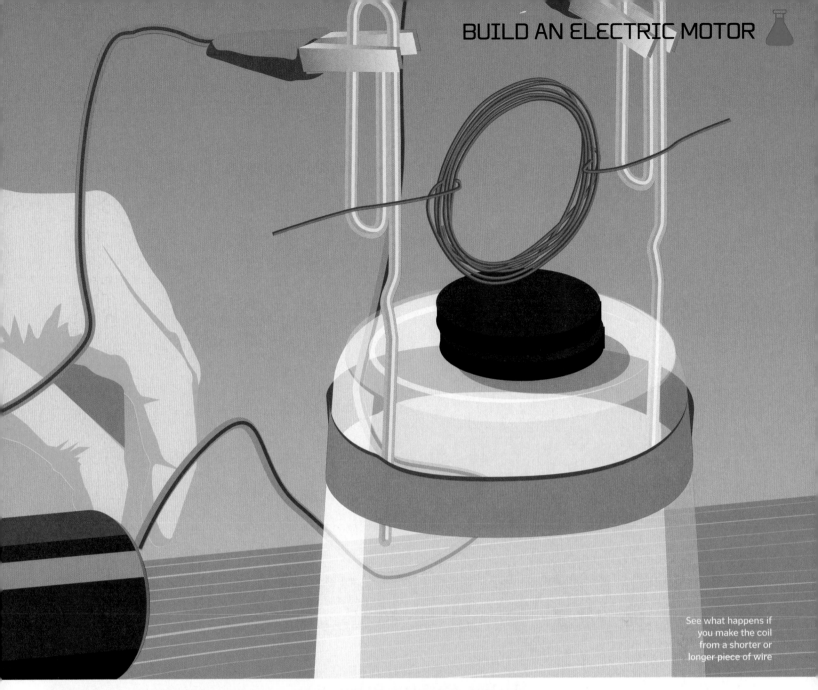

See what happens if you make the coil from a shorter or longer piece of wire

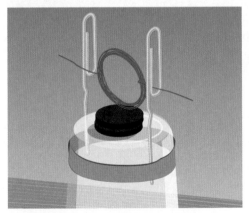

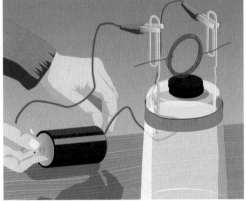

4 Insert your coil and magnet

Place two disc magnets in the centre of the plastic cup's base, one on top of the other. Next, rest your coil in the paper clip loops and adjust the height of the paper clips so that the coil is able to spin and just clears the magnets. It's important to adjust the coil so that it will remain balanced and centred when it spins on the paper clips, as this is key to the overall motor's function.

5 Finish your motor assembly

Attach a clip cable to each paper clip and hold the opposite ends of each cable to either end of the battery. The coil should spin and will align with the magnets due to the current you've created. If the coil doesn't spin, you may need to turn off the current once the coil and magnets are aligned. This can be achieved by painting the top half of one of the wires' two bare ends with a permanent marker.

"The coil should spin and will align with the magnets due to the current you've created"

SUMMARY

This simple experiment is a great way to see how a magnetic field is generated by an electric current. Using a permanent magnet enables the magnetic field to be attracted or repelled which causes movement in the wire that is carrying an electric current.

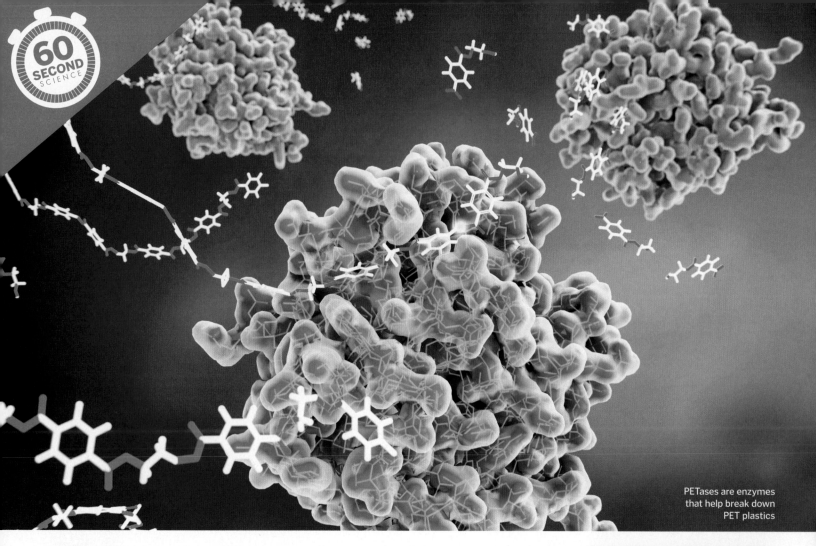

PETases are enzymes that help break down PET plastics

Enzymes

MEET THE MOLECULES THAT REGULATE THE BIOCHEMICAL REACTIONS IN OUR BODIES

Enzymes are often called 'biological catalysts', and their job is to speed up chemical reactions. You are full of dissolved chemicals with the potential to come together or separate to form the biological building blocks that you need to stay alive, but the reactions happen too slowly on their own.

Enzymes are molecules with 'active sites' that lock on to other molecules, bringing them close together so that they can react, or bending their structures so that they can combine or break apart more easily. The enzymes themselves do not actually get involved in the reactions; they just help them to happen faster.

Some of the most well-known enzymes are the ones in your digestive system. These are important for breaking down the molecules in your food. However, these aren't the only enzymes in your body. There are others responsible for building molecules, snipping molecules, tidying up when molecules are no longer needed, and some even help to destroy invading pathogens.

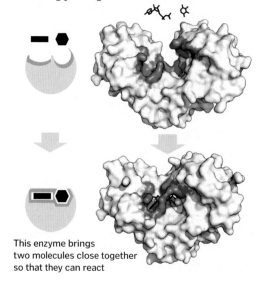

This enzyme brings two molecules close together so that they can react

BACKGROUND

Your body is like a walking, talking biochemical reactor, and enzymes are the catalysts. Enzymes are molecules that boost the rate of chemical reactions by bringing other molecules together so that they can react.

INDUSTRIAL ENZYMES

Enzymes are used for many different processes in agriculture, cosmetics, the food industry and more.

Perhaps their most well-known application is in biological washing detergents. These contain digestive enzymes (either one or a mixture of proteases, amylases and lipases) to help break down stains when washing clothes at lower temperatures.

Enzymes can also used when brewing beer; amylase is used to help turn starch into maltose and glucose, which yeast then feed on to start the alcoholic fermentation process.

Lipases are naturally found in unpasteurised milk, and can be used in the dairy industry to help produce cheeses. By breaking down fat globules into fatty acids, lipases can help improve the flavour of a cheese and play a role in the ripening process.

Enzymes can only be used in certain conditions. Extremes of temperature, pH and other chemicals can cause them to 'denature' – changing their shapes so the active sites no longer work.

DIGESTIVE ENZYMES

Find out which proteins help us break down our food

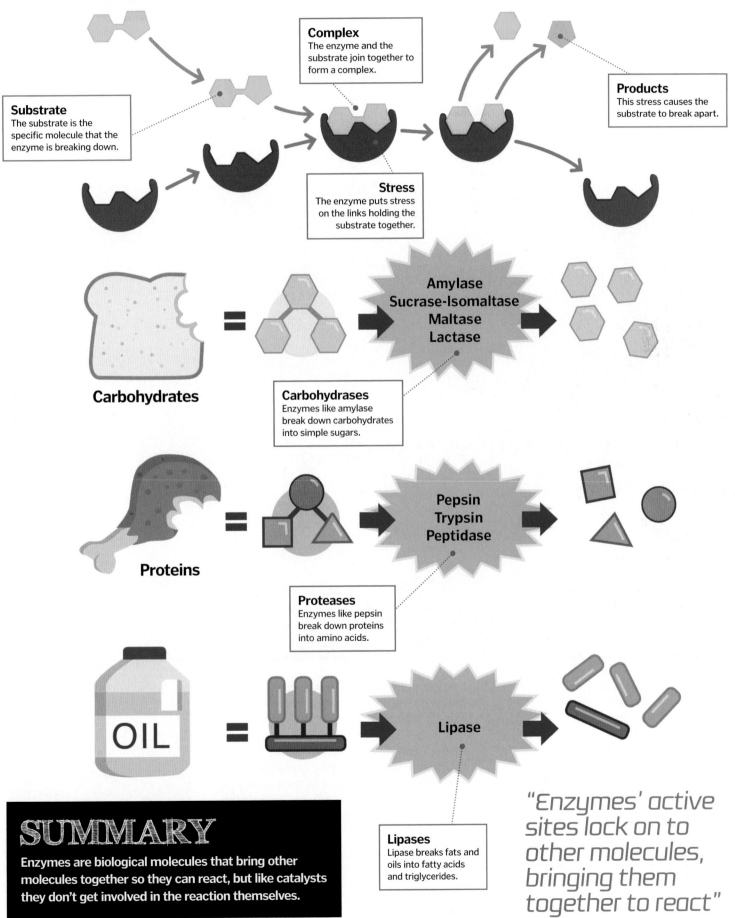

Substrate
The substrate is the specific molecule that the enzyme is breaking down.

Complex
The enzyme and the substrate join together to form a complex.

Stress
The enzyme puts stress on the links holding the substrate together.

Products
This stress causes the substrate to break apart.

Carbohydrates

Amylase
Sucrase-Isomaltase
Maltase
Lactase

Carbohydrases
Enzymes like amylase break down carbohydrates into simple sugars.

Proteins

Pepsin
Trypsin
Peptidase

Proteases
Enzymes like pepsin break down proteins into amino acids.

OIL

Lipase

Lipases
Lipase breaks fats and oils into fatty acids and triglycerides.

SUMMARY

Enzymes are biological molecules that bring other molecules together so they can react, but like catalysts they don't get involved in the reaction themselves.

"Enzymes' active sites lock on to other molecules, bringing them together to react"

60 SECOND SCIENCE

How plants transport water

PLANTS MIGHT LOOK STATIC, BUT THEY'RE HYDRAULIC ENGINEERS THAT ARE ALWAYS AT WORK

A plant's roots take in water and minerals from the soil as they move from the damp ground into the dry plant through a permeable layer. The longer they grow, the more surface area they have for absorption, and, amazingly, they can even grow in the direction of the wettest patches – a process called hydrotropism.

Plants rely on physics to get water from the ground to their leaves. Xylem tubes, made out of dead cells, are strong tubes running the whole length of the plant. As openings on the leaves (known as stomata) open to allow carbon dioxide in, water evaporates through transpiration. More water molecules are drawn up from further down the xylem tube to replace it and to balance out the difference in pressure, sticking to the molecules ahead of them and producing an effect similar to sucking on a drinking straw. On sunny and windy days, water evaporates from the leaves at a higher rate, so more is pulled up from the roots to counteract this.

> "Plants rely on physics to get water from the ground to their leaves"

BACKGROUND

Water is vital to plants. From growth and photosynthesis to flowering and keeping their leaves in shape, they need it for everything. To make sure they're getting enough of the stuff, plants have evolved an efficient water transport system.

LIVING WITHOUT WATER

When there's no rain and the soil is drying up, plants have to adapt to survive. By keeping their stomata closed during the hottest part of the day they can reduce transpiration, but with no carbon dioxide entering the leaves they can't photosynthesise to produce sugars. When temperatures drop at night, stomata can be opened to let carbon dioxide in while losing as little water as possible.

Some plants are used to coping with water scarcity. These species grow extremely long roots, and their leaves are either fleshy and covered in a waxy layer or reduced to spines to minimise water loss through evaporation. When rain does arrive, some species can store the water in tubers or bulbs under the ground for later use.

FROM THE GROUND UP

With this effective system, the tallest tree can get water to its leaves

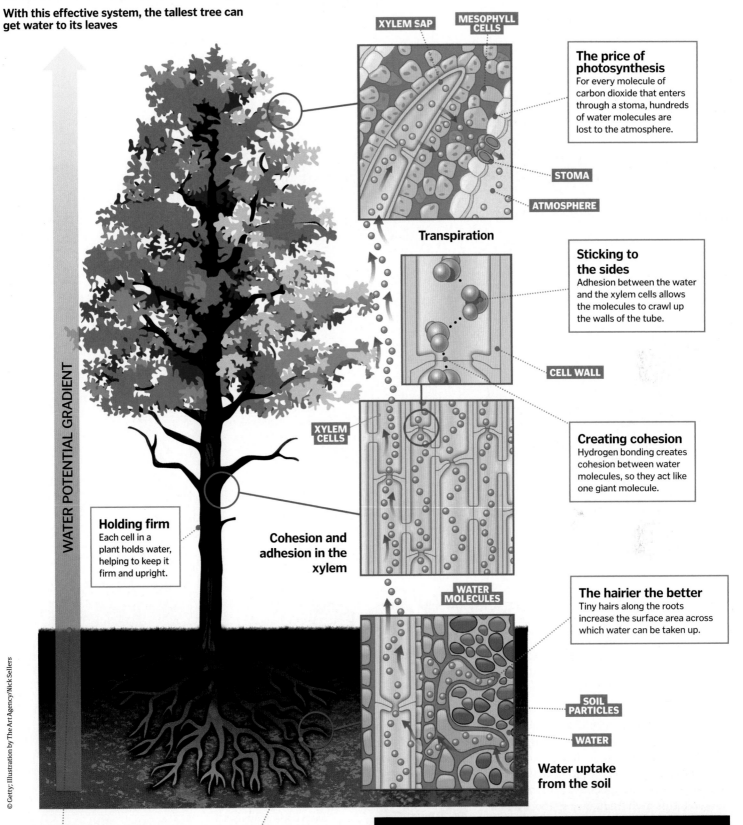

XYLEM SAP

MESOPHYLL CELLS

The price of photosynthesis
For every molecule of carbon dioxide that enters through a stoma, hundreds of water molecules are lost to the atmosphere.

STOMA

ATMOSPHERE

Transpiration

Sticking to the sides
Adhesion between the water and the xylem cells allows the molecules to crawl up the walls of the tube.

CELL WALL

Creating cohesion
Hydrogen bonding creates cohesion between water molecules, so they act like one giant molecule.

XYLEM CELLS

WATER POTENTIAL GRADIENT

Holding firm
Each cell in a plant holds water, helping to keep it firm and upright.

Cohesion and adhesion in the xylem

WATER MOLECULES

The hairier the better
Tiny hairs along the roots increase the surface area across which water can be taken up.

SOIL PARTICLES

WATER

Water uptake from the soil

© Getty; Illustration by The Art Agency/Nick Sellers

The water potential gradient
Water moves along a gradient, from damp soil to the outer part of the leaf where moisture is being lost.

The root cause
A network of roots spreads through the soil to absorb as much water as possible.

SUMMARY

Plants take up water from the soil through their roots. A difference in pressure between the top leaves and the bottom roots means that water molecules are drawn up through the length of the plant through its xylem tubes.

Sound waves

THE PHYSICS BEHIND THE NOISES YOU HEAR

 The frequency of sound waves is measured in hertz (Hz). Humans can only hear sounds between 20 and 20,000 Hz, as above this they are too high-pitched for our ears to register. However, this high frequency sound, known as ultrasound, can be heard by certain animals, including dogs and cats, and is very useful in medicine.

When ultrasound waves reach a boundary between two substances that have different densities, some of them are reflected back, a bit like an echo. By measuring the time it takes for the waves to bounce back, the distance to the boundary can be calculated. This is used to scan babies in the womb, as the boundary between the fluid in the womb and the baby's soft tissue can be used to create an image of the unborn child.

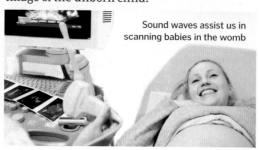
Sound waves assist us in scanning babies in the womb

BACKGROUND

Sound is created by vibrations passing through particles in solids, liquids and gases. These vibrations create waves and when these reach your ears, they are interpreted by your brain as sound.

Sound waves are longitudinal, which means they vibrate in the same direction as they travel, and can reflect off certain surfaces to create an echo. The shape of a sound wave can be shown by an oscilloscope machine and reveals a lot about the kind of sound created.

THE SPEED OF SOUND

The speed of a sound wave depends on what it is passing through. It travels through air at about 340 metres per second, but moves over four times faster through water and quicker still through certain solids.

However, it is still not as fast as light, which travels through air at just under 300,000,000 metres per second. This is why you can sometimes see the source of a sound before you hear the noise itself. If an object travels faster than the speed of sound, it forces the sound waves it creates together into one shockwave. This is interpreted by your brain as a loud sonic boom, and is what you hear when an aircraft breaks the sound barrier or when a whip cracks.

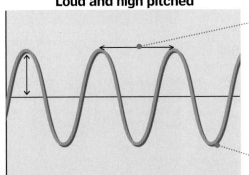

CALCULATING THE SPEED OF SOUND

A simple sound experiment you can try at home

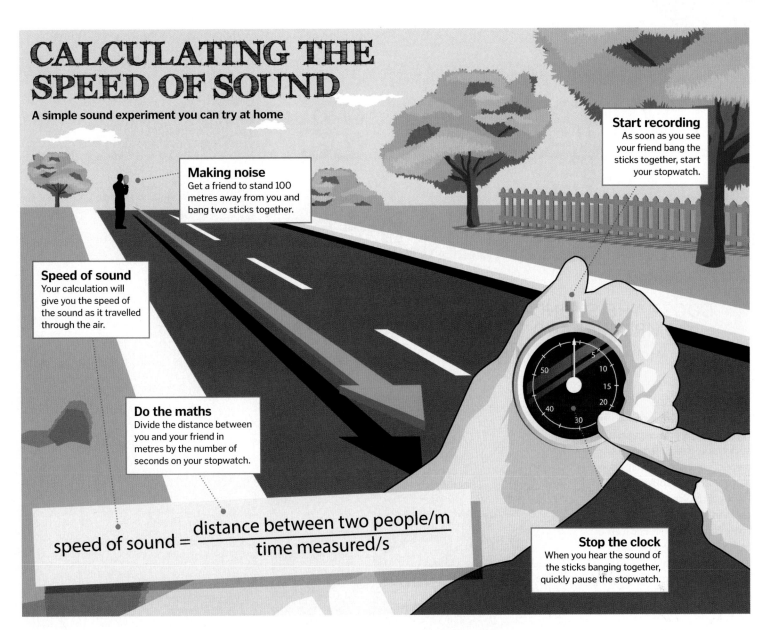

Making noise
Get a friend to stand 100 metres away from you and bang two sticks together.

Start recording
As soon as you see your friend bang the sticks together, start your stopwatch.

Speed of sound
Your calculation will give you the speed of the sound as it travelled through the air.

Do the maths
Divide the distance between you and your friend in metres by the number of seconds on your stopwatch.

Stop the clock
When you hear the sound of the sticks banging together, quickly pause the stopwatch.

$$\text{speed of sound} = \frac{\text{distance between two people/m}}{\text{time measured/s}}$$

SOUND WAVES EXPLAINED

What do the wiggly lines actually mean?

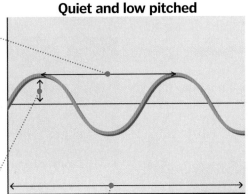

Quiet and low pitched

Loud and high pitched

Wavelength
The wavelength is the distance between two identical points (ie the peaks) of two sound waves next to each other.

Pitch
The shorter the wavelength, the higher the frequency of the wave and the higher the pitch of the sound created.

Amplitude
The amplitude is the maximum height of the sound wave from its resting position.

Volume
The greater the amplitude of the wave, the louder the sound created.

Frequency
The frequency is the number of sound waves created per second.

SUMMARY

Sound is vibrations through air, liquids or solids that are converted by your brain into electrical signals. The shape of the sound waves determines the volume and pitch of the sound.

©Illustration by Ed Crooks

Make a speaker

BOOST THE SOUND FROM YOUR PHONE OR COMPUTER, AND LEARN MORE ABOUT MAGNETISM WITH THIS PROJECT

The speaker works because the electric current generates a magnetic field

1 Coil the wire

For this experiment you'll need copper wire, a large paper cup, sticky tape, a disc magnet, a firm piece of cardboard, paperclips, an audio jack, and a soldering iron.

To start making your speaker, take the disc magnet and wrap some copper wire around it six or seven times. You will need at least ten centimetres of wire left at each end. Slide the coil off the magnet and tape it to the bottom of the paper cup, with one end of the wire trailing over each edge of the cup. This will soon become an electromagnet for your speaker.

2 Secure the magnet

Next, take the magnet and tape it to one side of a firm piece of cardboard. Make the cardboard stronger by straightening out a paperclip and taping it securely to the other side. Fold both ends of the cardboard so the whole piece sits neatly on the bottom of the cup – you should end up with a U-shaped piece with the magnet on the inside of the U.

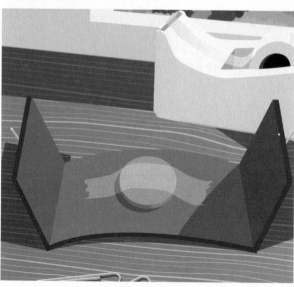

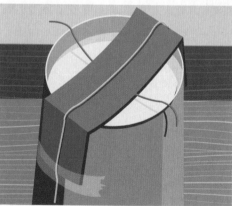

3 Attach and secure

Tape the cardboard to the cup as securely as possible. You don't want the magnet to move when the music is playing, as it will lessen the effect of the speaker – the speaker will push an electric current through the wire coil, making it magnetic. This will make it move (and the bottom of the cup) to create vibrations in the air, which we hear as sound waves!

"When you play music, the copper wire becomes an electromagnet"

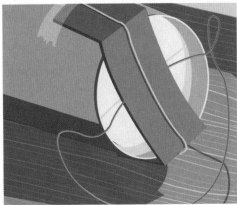

4 Solder it

You now need an audio jack so you can connect the speaker to your music device. There will be two wires inside the jack's cable, and you need to ask an adult to help you use a soldering iron to attach these to the two copper wires you left trailing over the edge of the cup. It doesn't matter which way they are connected, as long as they are attached.

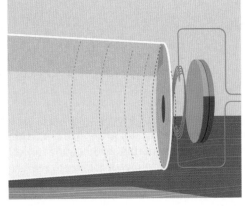

5 Pump it up!

You can create a cardboard case for the speaker if you wish, but it should work perfectly well without. When you play your music, the copper wire becomes an electromagnet that attracts and repels from the second magnet. This makes the base of the cup vibrate, and it creates sound waves, which bounce off the inside of the cup and become amplified.

SUMMARY

The key here is magnetism; the wire coil becomes an electromagnet when a current flows through it. This causes it to rapidly change between being positively charged and negatively charged, so it is attracted and repelled by the magnet over and over again, creating vibrations. This is how every speaker works on a basic level, making it surprisingly easy to recreate at home like this.

The quality won't be able to match shop-bought speakers, but this is a great way to understand how the technology works.

The pH scale

SORT YOUR ACIDS FROM YOUR ALKALIS WITH THIS SIMPLE 15-POINT CHART

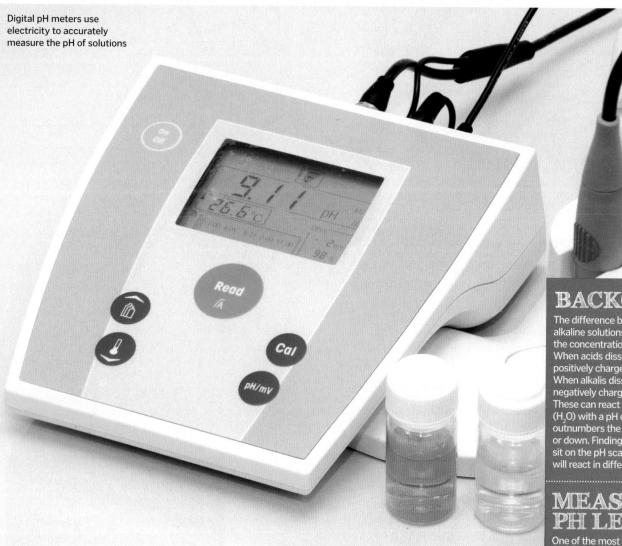

Digital pH meters use electricity to accurately measure the pH of solutions

The pH of a solution tells you what concentration of hydrogen ions it contains. The scale runs from 0 to 14. In mathematical terms the pH number is the negative logarithm of the concentration of hydrogen ions in a solution. Put simply, for every step up you go on the pH scale, there are ten times fewer hydrogen ions in solution. At pH 0, the concentration of hydrogen ions is 1 mol dm^{-3}, at pH 1, it's 0.1 mol dm^{-3}, at pH 2, 0.01 mol dm^{-3} and so on.

Indicator solutions reveal the pH of unknown liquids because they change colour when they react with H$^+$ or OH$^-$ ions. The most well known indicator is litmus, which turns

red in acids and blue in alkaline solutions, but universal indicator gives an even clearer picture. It contains several indicator solutions, creating a rainbow of colours to represent different pH values.

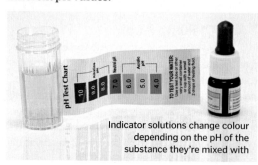

Indicator solutions change colour depending on the pH of the substance they're mixed with

BACKGROUND

The difference between acidic and alkaline solutions all comes down to the concentration of hydrogen ions. When acids dissolve, they release positively charged hydrogen ions (H$^+$). When alkalis dissolve, they release negatively charged hydroxyl ions (OH$^-$). These can react to form neutral water (H$_2$O) with a pH of 7, but if one outnumbers the other, the pH shifts up or down. Finding out where solutions sit on the pH scale can tell us how they will react in different situations.

MEASURING PH LEVELS

One of the most accurate ways to measure pH is with a digital pH meter. Rather than rely on matching the colours of an indicator solution, it gives a digital readout, measuring fractions of a point on the pH chart.

A digital pH meter has a probe that contains two electrodes; a glass electrode and a reference electrode. The glass electrode contains a solution of potassium chloride with a set number of hydrogen ions and a pH of 7. When a current passes through the probe, hydrogen ions from the glass electrode and hydrogen ions from the test solution interact with the glass. If the concentrations of hydrogen ions differ, it creates a difference in voltage. The meter measures this 'potential difference' and uses it to calculate the concentration of hydrogen ions in the test solution.

EVERYDAY pH

Universal indicator can tell you where everyday solutions sit on the pH scale

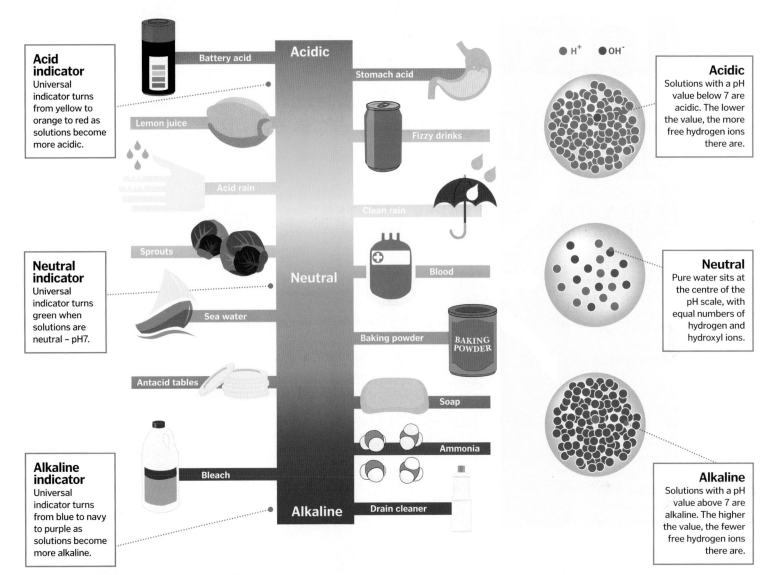

Acid indicator
Universal indicator turns from yellow to orange to red as solutions become more acidic.

Neutral indicator
Universal indicator turns green when solutions are neutral – pH7.

Alkaline indicator
Universal indicator turns from blue to navy to purple as solutions become more alkaline.

Battery acid
Lemon juice
Acid rain
Sprouts
Sea water
Antacid tables
Bleach

Acidic
Stomach acid
Fizzy drinks
Clean rain
Blood
Neutral
Baking powder
BAKING POWDER
Soap
Ammonia
Drain cleaner
Alkaline

● H⁺   ● OH⁻

Acidic
Solutions with a pH value below 7 are acidic. The lower the value, the more free hydrogen ions there are.

Neutral
Pure water sits at the centre of the pH scale, with equal numbers of hydrogen and hydroxyl ions.

Alkaline
Solutions with a pH value above 7 are alkaline. The higher the value, the fewer free hydrogen ions there are.

pH 7   pH 4

SUMMARY

The pH scale is a way to quantify how acidic or alkaline a solution is. Adding colour-changing indicator solutions tells us how many free hydrogen ions are present.

© Getty

Make pH paper

LEARN HOW TO MAKE PH PAPER AND TEST ACIDITY IN YOUR OWN KITCHEN

1 Prepare your cabbage

For this experiment you'll need a red cabbage, a saucepan and hob, some paper towels, scissors, test tubes, a test tube stand and a selection of household liquids (see Step 4).

First, the red cabbage needs to be prepared for cooking. Chop the cabbage into small pieces and place them into a saucepan. Cover the chopped cabbage with water and then heat the pan until the water starts boiling. Turn the heat down and allow the cabbage to simmer for about 20 minutes, stirring every now and then.

2 Stain your paper towels

Once the cabbage has finished cooking, remove it from the heat and pour the saucepan's contents through a strainer, making sure the purple liquid is collected in a bowl. You will no longer need the cabbage itself so save it for a recipe.

Once the liquid is cool enough to handle, add the paper towels and stir. Leave them to soak up the liquid for five minutes, until they've taken on the liquid's purple colour.

The paper strips will change colour depending on the pH values of the liquids they're exposed to

3 Dry and cut your paper towel

Take each paper towel out of the liquid and place onto a cooling rack to dry off. Make sure you put something underneath the cooling rack to catch the drips from the paper towels, as these can stain the surface below. Once the papers are dry, cut them into rectangular strips roughly 1.5 centimetres wide. You are now ready to test the pH of your selection of different liquids.

4 Prepare your test liquids

It's now time to test out your pH strips! For this part you'll need the test tubes, stand and some household liquids. Some good liquids to use are lemon juice, milk, vinegar and dish soap as they have different pH values.

Fill each test tube by half with a test liquid, then dip one test strip into each and leave for a few minutes. Keep watching the tubes to see the strips change colour.

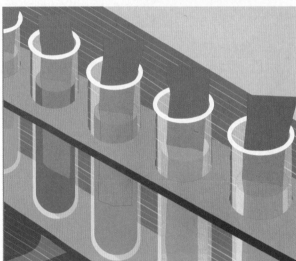

5 Record your findings

Once you're happy that the paper towel strips have spent sufficient time in the test liquids, you can remove them. If you can't do this with your fingers, use a wooden skewer.

You should record the colour of each strip immediately; as once they begin to dry the colours will often lighten and become less clear. You could even stick them onto your worksheet to keep.

SUMMARY

Red cabbage contains a pigment called anthocyanin, which is responsible for its colour. It's also present in leaves that become red or purple during the autumn. The changing colours you observed during this experiment show that anthocyanin is a good indicator of acids and bases. It will turn green or yellow when added to a base, but will become red or pink when added to an acid. In neutral liquids, it will remain purple.

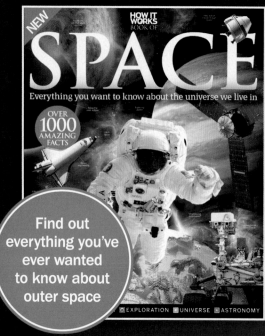

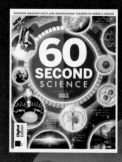

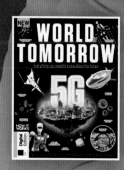
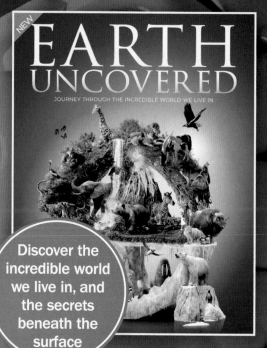

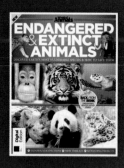
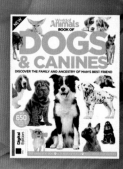

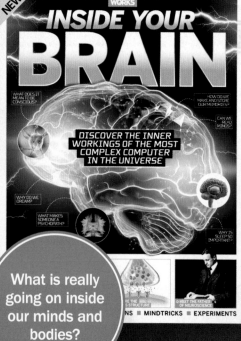
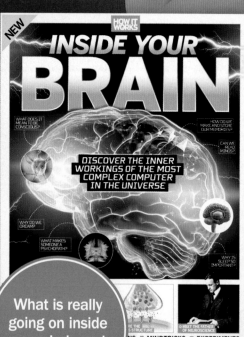
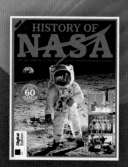

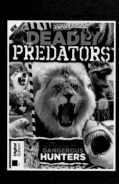

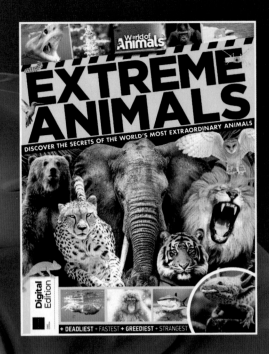
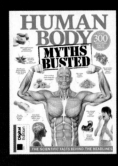
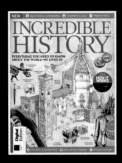

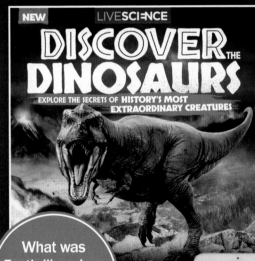

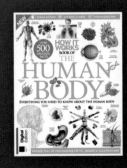
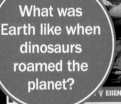